Monitoring, Simulation, Prevention and Remediation of Dense and Debris Flows II

WIT*PRESS*

WIT Press publishes leading books in Science and Technology.
Visit our website for the current list of titles.
www.witpress.com

WIT *eLibrary*

Home of the Transactions of the Wessex Institute.
Papers presented at Debris Flow II are archived in the WIT eLibrary in
volume 60 of WIT Transactions on Engineering Sciences (ISSN 1743-3533).
The WIT eLibrary provides the international scientific community with
immediate and permanent access to individual papers presented at WIT conferences.
http://library.witpress.com

SECOND INTERNATIONAL CONFERENCE ON
MONITORING, SIMULATION, PREVENTION AND
REMEDIATION OF DENSE AND DEBRIS FLOWS

DEBRIS FLOW II

CONFERENCE CHAIRMEN

D. de Wrachien
University of Milan, Italy

C.A. Brebbia
Wessex Institute of Technology, UK

M.A. Lenzi
University of Padova, Italy

INTERNATIONAL SCIENTIFIC ADVISORY COMMITTEE

G. Chambon
C. Chen
V. D'Agostino
V. Ferro
R. Garcia-Martinez
F. Gentile
J. Huebl
J.L. Lopez
G. Lorenzini
J. Martin-Duque
A. Nemdili
F. Wei

Organised by
Wessex Institute of Technology, UK

Sponsored by
WIT Transactions on Engineering Sciences
EurAgEng: European Society of Agricultural Engineers
CIGR: International Commission of Agricultural Engineers

WIT Transactions

Transactions Editor

Carlos Brebbia
Wessex Institute of Technology
Ashurst Lodge, Ashurst
Southampton SO40 7AA, UK
Email: carlos@wessex.ac.uk

Editorial Board

S K Chakrabarti Offshore Structure Analysis, USA

A H-D Cheng University of Mississippi, USA

J Chilton University of Lincoln, UK

C-L Chiu University of Pittsburgh, USA

H Choi Kangnung National University, Korea

A Cieslak Technical University of Lodz, Poland

S Clement Transport System Centre, Australia

M W Collins Brunel University, UK

J J Connor Massachusetts Institute of Technology, USA

M C Constantinou State University of New York at Buffalo, USA

D E Cormack University of Toronto, Canada

M Costantino Royal Bank of Scotland, UK

D F Cutler Royal Botanic Gardens, UK

W Czyczula Krakow University of Technology, Poland

M da Conceicao Cunha University of Coimbra, Portugal

A Davies University of Hertfordshire, UK

M Davis Temple University, USA

A B de Almeida Instituto Superior Tecnico, Portugal

E R de Arantes e Oliveira Instituto Superior Tecnico, Portugal

L De Biase University of Milan, Italy

R de Borst Delft University of Technology, Netherlands

G De Mey University of Ghent, Belgium

A De Montis Universita di Cagliari, Italy

A De Naeyer Universiteit Ghent, Belgium

W P De Wilde Vrije Universiteit Brussel, Belgium

L Debnath University of Texas-Pan American, USA

N J Dedios Mimbela Universidad de Cordoba, Spain

G Degrande Katholieke Universiteit Leuven, Belgium

S del Giudice University of Udine, Italy

G Deplano Universita di Cagliari, Italy

I Doltsinis University of Stuttgart, Germany

M Domaszewski Universite de Technologie de Belfort-Montbeliard, France

J Dominguez University of Seville, Spain

K Dorow Pacific Northwest National Laboratory, USA

W Dover University College London, UK

C Dowlen South Bank University, UK

J P du Plessis University of Stellenbosch, South Africa

R Duffell University of Hertfordshire, UK

A Ebel University of Cologne, Germany

E E Edoutos Democritus University of Thrace, Greece

G K Egan Monash University, Australia

K M Elawadly Alexandria University, Egypt

K-H Elmer Universitat Hannover, Germany

D Elms University of Canterbury, New Zealand

M E M El-Sayed Kettering University, USA

D M Elsom Oxford Brookes University, UK

A El-Zafrany Cranfield University, UK

F Erdogan Lehigh University, USA

F P Escrig University of Seville, Spain

D J Evans Nottingham Trent University, UK

J W Everett Rowan University, USA

M Faghri University of Rhode Island, USA

R A Falconer Cardiff University, UK

M N Fardis University of Patras, Greece

P Fedelinski Silesian Technical University, Poland

H J S Fernando Arizona State University, USA

S Finger Carnegie Mellon University, USA

J I Frankel University of Tennessee, USA

D M Fraser University of Cape Town, South Africa

M J Fritzler University of Calgary, Canada

U Gabbert Otto-von-Guericke Universitat Magdeburg, Germany

G Gambolati Universita di Padova, Italy

C J Gantes National Technical University of Athens, Greece

L Gaul Universitat Stuttgart, Germany

A Genco University of Palermo, Italy

N Georgantzis Universitat Jaume I, Spain

G S Gipson Oklahoma State University, USA

P Giudici Universita di Pavia, Italy

F Gomez Universidad Politecnica de Valencia, Spain

R **Gomez Martin** University of Granada, Spain

D **Goulias** University of Maryland, USA

K G **Goulias** Pennsylvania State University, USA

F **Grandori** Politecnico di Milano, Italy

W E **Grant** Texas A & M University, USA

S **Grilli** University of Rhode Island, USA

R H J **Grimshaw,** Loughborough University, UK

D **Gross** Technische Hochschule Darmstadt, Germany

R **Grundmann** Technische Universitat Dresden, Germany

A **Gualtierotti** IDHEAP, Switzerland

R C **Gupta** National University of Singapore, Singapore

J M **Hale** University of Newcastle, UK

K **Hameyer** Katholieke Universiteit Leuven, Belgium

C **Hanke** Danish Technical University, Denmark

K **Hayami** National Institute of Informatics, Japan

Y **Hayashi** Nagoya University, Japan

L **Haydock** Newage International Limited, UK

A H **Hendrickx** Free University of Brussels, Belgium

C **Herman** John Hopkins University, USA

S **Heslop** University of Bristol, UK

I **Hideaki** Nagoya University, Japan

D A **Hills** University of Oxford, UK

W F **Huebner** Southwest Research Institute, USA

J A C **Humphrey** Bucknell University, USA

M Y **Hussaini** Florida State University, USA

W **Hutchinson** Edith Cowan University, Australia

T H **Hyde** University of Nottingham, UK

M **Iguchi** Science University of Tokyo, Japan

D B **Ingham** University of Leeds, UK

L **Int Panis** VITO Expertisecentrum IMS, Belgium

N **Ishikawa** National Defence Academy, Japan

J **Jaafar** UiTm, Malaysia

W **Jager** Technical University of Dresden, Germany

Y **Jaluria** Rutgers University, USA

C M **Jefferson** University of the West of England, UK

P R **Johnston** Griffith University, Australia

D R H **Jones** University of Cambridge, UK

N **Jones** University of Liverpool, UK

D **Kaliampakos** National Technical University of Athens, Greece

N **Kamiya** Nagoya University, Japan

D L **Karabalis** University of Patras, Greece

M **Karlsson** Linkoping University, Sweden

T **Katayama** Doshisha University, Japan

K L **Katsifarakis** Aristotle University of Thessaloniki, Greece

J T **Katsikadelis** National Technical University of Athens, Greece

E **Kausel** Massachusetts Institute of Technology, USA

H **Kawashima** The University of Tokyo, Japan

B A **Kazimee** Washington State University, USA

S **Kim** University of Wisconsin-Madison, USA

D **Kirkland** Nicholas Grimshaw & Partners Ltd, UK

E **Kita** Nagoya University, Japan

A S **Kobayashi** University of Washington, USA

T **Kobayashi** University of Tokyo, Japan

D **Koga** Saga University, Japan

A **Konrad** University of Toronto, Canada

S **Kotake** University of Tokyo, Japan

A N **Kounadis** National Technical University of Athens, Greece

W B **Kratzig** Ruhr Universitat Bochum, Germany

T **Krauthammer** Penn State University, USA

C-H **Lai** University of Greenwich, UK

M **Langseth** Norwegian University of Science and Technology, Norway

B S **Larsen** Technical University of Denmark, Denmark

F **Lattarulo,** Politecnico di Bari, Italy

A **Lebedev** Moscow State University, Russia

L J **Leon** University of Montreal, Canada

D **Lewis** Mississippi State University, USA

S **Ighobashi** University of California Irvine, USA

K-C Lin University of New Brunswick, Canada

A A Liolios Democritus University of Thrace, Greece

S Lomov Katholieke Universiteit Leuven, Belgium

J W S Longhurst University of the West of England, UK

G Loo The University of Auckland, New Zealand

J Lourenco Universidade do Minho, Portugal

J E Luco University of California at San Diego, USA

H Lui State Seismological Bureau Harbin, China

C J Lumsden University of Toronto, Canada

L Lundqvist Division of Transport and Location Analysis, Sweden

T Lyons Murdoch University, Australia

Y-W Mai University of Sydney, Australia

M Majowiecki University of Bologna, Italy

D Malerba Università degli Studi di Bari, Italy

G Manara University of Pisa, Italy

B N Mandal Indian Statistical Institute, India

Ü Mander University of Tartu, Estonia

H A Mang Technische Universitat Wien, Austria,

G D, Manolis, Aristotle University of Thessaloniki, Greece

W J Mansur COPPE/UFRJ, Brazil

N Marchettini University of Siena, Italy

J D M Marsh Griffith University, Australia

J F Martin-Duque Universidad Complutense, Spain

T Matsui Nagoya University, Japan

G Mattrisch DaimlerChrysler AG, Germany

F M Mazzolani University of Naples "Federico II", Italy

K McManis University of New Orleans, USA

A C Mendes Universidade de Beira Interior, Portugal,

R A Meric Research Institute for Basic Sciences, Turkey

J Mikielewicz Polish Academy of Sciences, Poland

N Milic-Frayling Microsoft Research Ltd, UK

R A W Mines University of Liverpool, UK

C A Mitchell University of Sydney, Australia

K Miura Kajima Corporation, Japan

A Miyamoto Yamaguchi University, Japan

T Miyoshi Kobe University, Japan

G Molinari University of Genoa, Italy

T B Moodie University of Alberta, Canada

D B Murray Trinity College Dublin, Ireland

G Nakhaeizadeh DaimlerChrysler AG, Germany

M B Neace Mercer University, USA

D Necsulescu University of Ottawa, Canada

F Neumann University of Vienna, Austria

S-I Nishida Saga University, Japan

H Nisitani Kyushu Sangyo University, Japan

B Notaros University of Massachusetts, USA

P O'Donoghue University College Dublin, Ireland

R O O'Neill Oak Ridge National Laboratory, USA

M Ohkusu Kyushu University, Japan

G Oliveto Universitá di Catania, Italy

R Olsen Camp Dresser & McKee Inc., USA

E Oñate Universitat Politecnica de Catalunya, Spain

K Onishi Ibaraki University, Japan

P H Oosthuizen Queens University, Canada

E L Ortiz Imperial College London, UK

E Outa Waseda University, Japan

A S Papageorgiou Rensselaer Polytechnic Institute, USA

J Park Seoul National University, Korea

G Passerini Universita delle Marche, Italy

B C Patten, University of Georgia, USA

G Pelosi University of Florence, Italy

G G Penelis, Aristotle University of Thessaloniki, Greece

W Perrie Bedford Institute of Oceanography, Canada

R Pietrabissa Politecnico di Milano, Italy

H Pina Instituto Superior Tecnico, Portugal

M F Platzer Naval Postgraduate School, USA

D Poljak University of Split, Croatia

Monitoring, Simulation, Prevention and Remediation of Dense Debris Flows II

Editors

D. de Wrachien
University of Milan, Italy

C.A. Brebbia
Wessex Institute of Technology, UK

M.A. Lenzi
University of Padova, Italy

WITPRESS Southampton, Boston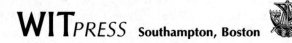

D. de Wrachien
University of Milan, Italy

C.A. Brebbia
Wessex Institute of Technology, UK

M.A. Lenzi
University of Padova, Italy

Published by

WIT Press
Ashurst Lodge, Ashurst, Southampton, SO40 7AA, UK
Tel: 44 (0) 238 029 3223; Fax: 44 (0) 238 029 2853
E-Mail: witpress@witpress.com
http://www.witpress.com

For USA, Canada and Mexico

Computational Mechanics Inc
25 Bridge Street, Billerica, MA 01821, USA
Tel: 978 667 5841; Fax: 978 667 7582
E-Mail: infousa@witpress.com
http://www.witpress.com

British Library Cataloguing-in-Publication Data

A Catalogue record for this book is available
from the British Library

ISBN: 978-1-84564-118-4
ISSN: 1746-4471 (print)
ISSN: 1743-3533 (online)

*The texts of the papers in this volume were set
individually by the authors or under their supervision.
Only minor corrections to the text may have been carried
out by the publisher.*

Preface

This book contains papers presented at the Second International Conference on Debris Flow including Debris Flow Monitoring, Modelling, Hazard Assessment, Mitigation Measures, Case Studies and Extreme Events, Erosion, Slope Instability and Sediment Transport, held in the New Forest, UK in 2008 and organised by the Wessex Institute of Technology, with the co-sponsorship of EurAgEng (European Society of Agricultural Engineers) and CIGR (International Commission of Agricultural Engineering).

Due to the increased frequency with which debris and hyper-concentrated flows occur and the impact they have on both the environment and human life, these extreme events and related processes have attracted increasing attention from research groups, land planning and management professionals

The objective of the Meeting was to provide a forum for engineers, scientists and managers from laboratories, industry, government and academia to interchange knowledge and expertise in the field of dense and hyper-concentrated flows. A full understanding of these phenomena leads to an integrated risk management approach which provides measures for preventing a hazard turning into a natural disaster.

The book contains the following sessions: Debris Flow Mitigation; Debris Flow Modelling; Case Studies; Sediment Transport and Debris Flow including Woody Debris.

The Editors are grateful to all the authors for their excellent contributions as well as to the members of the International Scientific Advisory Committee for the review of both the abstracts and the papers included in this book. The quality of the material makes this Volume a most valuable and up-to-date tool for professionals, scientists and managers to appreciate the state-of-the-art in this important field of knowledge.

The Editors
The New Forest, 2008

Contents

Section 3: Case studies

Section 4: Sediment transport and debris flow including woody debris
Special session organised by D. De Wrachien and M. A. Lenzi

Section 1
Debris flow mitigation

Infrasound measurements of debris flow

J. Hübl[1], S. C. Zhang[2] & A. Kogelnig[1]
[1]Institute of Mountain Risk Engineering, Department Civil Engineering
and Natural Hazards, University of Natural Resources & Applied Life
Sciences, Vienna, Austria
[2]Institute of Mountain Hazards and Environment, Chinese Academy of
Sciences and Ministry of Water Resources, Chengdu, China

Abstract

Processes such as wind, avalanches, traffic and debris flow are sources of sub-audible sounds in the low frequency infrasonic spectrum. These signals have the ability to propagate kilometres from the debris flow source and provide a basis for developing wide area automated monitoring systems that can operate in locations unaffected by the process activity. This study focuses on naturally occurring infrasound produced by a 3 days debris flow event in July 2007, in the Jiangjia Gully, Yunnan, China. The debris flows had a big variety in terms of the amount of discharge and furthermore they differ from very fluid surges up to more solid surges with a density of 2000kg/m³. The data was monitored with two different microphones, a custom made Chinese Sensor and a standard infrasound measuring microphone from a German Company. Contemporary video recording and photographing took place for visual validation of the acoustic signals. The aim is to specify the debris flow signal out of environmental interferences through the use of digital filtering and frequency analysis.
Keywords: infrasound monitoring, debris flow, frequency spectrum, field study.

1 Introduction

Rapid mass movements like debris flows, debris floods and intensive bedload transport are periodic or episodic phenomena in alpine regions. Due to the fast socio-economic development of mountain regions, these processes which are at the intersection between the natural environment and the environment formed and controlled by human activities increasingly become a hazard for people and

WIT Transactions on Engineering Sciences, Vol 60, © 2008 WIT Press
www.witpress.com, ISSN 1743-3533 (on-line)
doi:10.2495/DEB080011

property. Though considerable research has been carried out in the last decades to understand processes like debris flows [1–3], there is still a lot unknown. This is partly due to the scarcity of observations and data of real events.

Infrasonic sound is too low frequent to hear; its acoustic spectrum covers frequencies below 20Hz which are generated by the compressibility of the air. These low frequency signals have the ability to propagate long distances through the atmosphere with a velocity of 344m/s which is about the same as that of audible sound [4]. This is due to the low absorption of the air and the high reflectivity of the ground. Infrasound monitoring systems are used to detect hazards such as avalanches [5, 6, 8–10], landslides [7], nuclear explosions [11] and debris flows [4]. Debris flow generated infrasound signals are of significant amplitude and occupy a relatively noise free band in the low infrasonic spectrum (8–12Hz). This study analysis and demonstrates characteristic infrasound signals of debris flow monitored during an event between the 25 and 30 July 2007 in the Jiangjia Gully, Yunnan, China. This work is possible due to cooperation with the Institute of Mountain Hazards and Environment of the Chinese Academy of Science and Ministry of Water Resources, with whom we share a database of infrasonic debris flow signals.

2 Infrasound signals of debris flow

The monitoring of natural mass movements is not always possible given the sporadic character of the events and the difficulty of accessing the affected areas and the bad weather conditions that usually accompany these phenomena. Monitoring systems based on seismic signals (frequency 30–80Hz; velocity 1000m/s) are quite common and have been used to study debris flows for many years. Various previous studies on debris flow [e.g. 12–17] have already shown that it is possible to detect and monitor these processes with geophones and to distinguish them from other seismic sources. To overcome a major disadvantage of geophones in connection with debris flow, namely the limited spatial propagation of seismic waves, this study focuses on infrasonic signals. It is well known that a debris flow produces vibrations in the ground when it moves around a channel; these vibrations then produce sound waves, containing both audible sound (20 Hz–20 kHz) and inaudible sound, infrasound, with frequencies less than 20 Hz [4]. Infrasound is expected to be generated by the violent surge front and the collision (or abrasion) between debris flow and the channel loose boundary [18]. In consequence, the analysis and inter comparison of the infrasound signals generated by various debris flows can provide useful information of these phenomena.

3 Study site and monitoring system

3.1 Geographical and geological overview

The catchment area of the Jiangjia Gully, Yunnan, China covers 48,6 km². It is characterised by steep slopes, numerous areas of landslides and collapses, poor vegetation cover and intensive rainfall. The elevation level varies from 1050m where the Jiangjia Ravine joins the Xiaojiang River up to 3145m, which is the highest point in the catchment, fig 1. In this basin there are 154 gullies whose widths vary from narrow 50m up to 200m and with a variation in gradient from 20% to 60%. The sediments for the debris flow are generated by landslides which supply the channel beds with materials. The mixture of sediments can be divided into two main classes: one is about 20mm in mean diameter and the

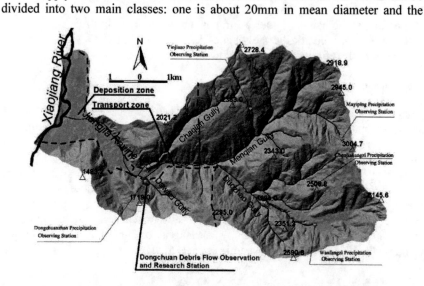

Figure 1:   Overview of the Jiangjia Ravine (Source: IMHE).

Figure 2:   Debris flow surge passing the observation station.

other is less than 2mm [19]. These are easily eroded by the water stream after a rainfall. The correlation between the occurrence of debris flow and 10-minute rainfall is very good and moreover, debris flow occurs when rainfall intensity increases and does not when intensity decreases [19]. The characteristics of the processes occurring in the Jiangjia Ravine can be described as wave trains of debris flow occurring for a period of time without any surges in between. Shortest burst last 10 to 20 minutes but big events can hold up to 10 hours.

Looking at the height of such a surge it can be up to 3m in the wide river bed with the biggest velocities at the tongue-like head (5–10m/s). Due to these facts the area is perfect for debris flow monitoring purposes.

3.2 Infrasound Monitoring Station (IMS)

One of the most successful studies was carried out by Zhang [4]. He developed an infrasound warning system (DFW-I Model) and applied it successfully to detect over 60 debris surges in Jiangjia Gullies (China) with a warning time of 10–30 minutes.

During the events in July 2007 the data was monitored with two different microphones: The DFW-I III Model, custom made by our Chinese partners and the WME 960H, a German made standard infrasound measuring microphone. Both sensors are based on the capacitive pressure transducer principle and have similar specifications; characterised by a sensitivity of 50mV/Pa, wide frequency response (3–100Hz) and wide dynamic range (150dB).

3.3 Data analysis

The methodologies adopted for data analysis include the Fast Fourier Transformation and the Continuous Wavelet Transform (CWT). Traditionally, the Fourier Transformation has been the general approach to analyze signal data in frequency domain for investigating its energy frequency distribution [20, 21]. The demand of FFT is system linearity, periodicity and stationarity; unfortunately most data monitored from natural phenomena do not fulfill this requirement. Therefore spurious harmonic components are induced that cause energy spreading and mislead the energy-frequency distribution for nonlinear and non-stationary data.

The Continuous Wavelet Transform (CWT) is used to decompose a signal into wavelets, small oscillations that are highly localized in time. Whereas the Fourier transform decomposes a signal into infinite length sins [22] and cosines, effectively losing all time-localization information, the CWT's basis functions are scaled and shifted versions of the time-localized mother wavelet. The CWT is used to construct a time-frequency representation of a signal that offers very good time and frequency localization e.g. [23, 24].

4   Results and discussion

The results shown below have been monitored on the 25.07.2007. To compare and evaluate the signals, they have been recorded simultaneously with two infrasound sensors. On this day, especially in the time between 12.30am and 1.20 pm, regular debris flow was observed. The data is representing a time gap of 30 seconds where various surges occurred. In the following figures the top blue graph is data monitored with the Gefell Mk 222 infrasound sensor and the bottom green graph is data monitored with the China Mk 224 sensor.

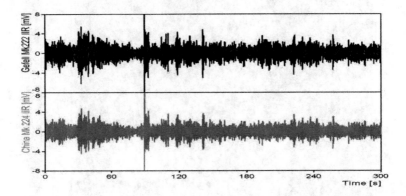

Figure 3:   Raw data of debris flow during flow event (25.07.2007).

Data were recorded with a sampling frequency of 100 Hz. The predominant frequency, as it appears in figure 5, is around 10Hz. There is another peak around 30Hz, which is not in the infrasonic range. As figures 4 and 5 illustrate, there are strong correlations throughout the whole analysis between the two different sensors. The following spectra were calculated using both the FFT and the CWT algorithms.

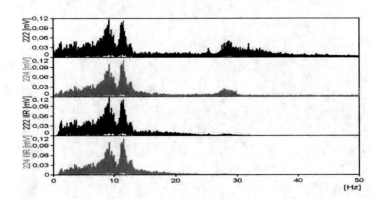

Figure 4:   Frequency spectrum of the unfiltered (top) and filtered signal (bottom).

The spectra prove, no matter if FFT or CWT analysis, that infrasonic sound is emitted by debris flow. The signals possess a predominant frequency around 10Hz. It is also possible to detect different surges passing the sensor.

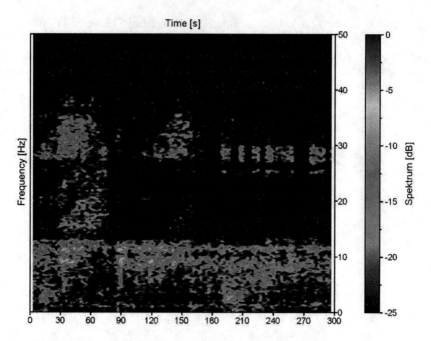

Figure 5:   FFT spectra of unfiltered data recorded by Mk 222.

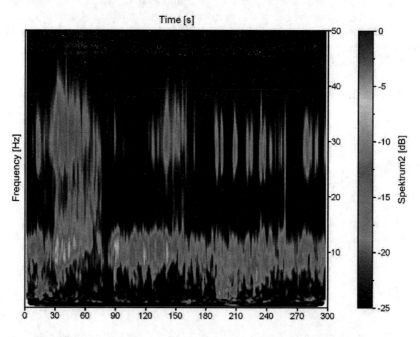

Figure 6:   CWT spectra of unfiltered data recorded by Mk 222.

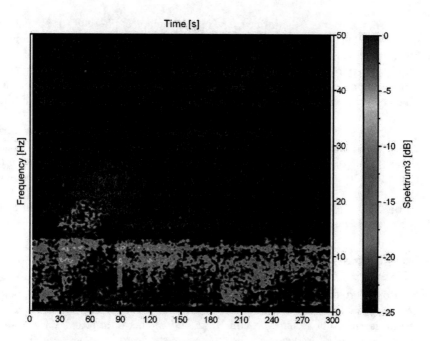

Figure 7:   FFT spectra of filtered data recorded by Mk 222.

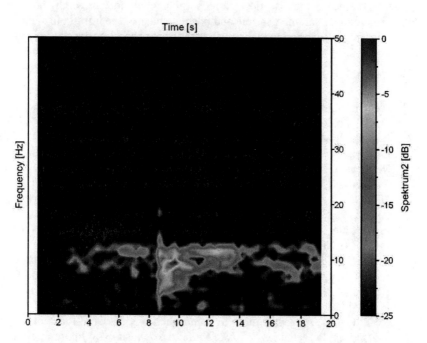

Figure 8:   FFT spectra of filtered data of a single surge recorded by Mk 222.

In order to decrease the influence of interfering noise, filtering was applied to the collected data. The filtering, in the range from 1-20Hz, was done by a fourth order Butterworth band pass filter. The results clearly demonstrate that it was possible to remove the acoustic signals of debris flow around 30Hz. Although we expected improvement of signal intensity in the infrasonic range it did not occur. This could be explained by the low interfering infrasonic noise existing in the Jiangjia Ravine.

Figure 9 shows a time sequence (seconds 80–100) of the previous discussed data. Through the FFT analysis the relationship between the frequencies of peak intensity and a single surge is shown in figure 9. The greater the discharge of a debris flow the higher is the amplitude of the signal and predominant frequency varies within a bigger range. As the surge passes the observation station, the energy with the frequencies between 5–15 Hz is intensified. Moving further away peak frequencies tend to concentrate around 10 Hz.

5   Summary and conclusions

Infrasound produced by debris flow is explored in this study by examining field data monitored in Jiangjia Gully, Yunnan, China. The signal shows two peaks, one in the infrasound range, around 10Hz, and another one around 30Hz. More signal intensity is produced in the infrasonic spectrum. It is also possible to detect a single surge passing the observation station. Therefore it can be used to detect and record debris flow for warning and for research purposes. Furthermore other natural disasters and phenomena produce infrasonic signals as well [4]. Thus it is needed to distinguish them from debris flow before.

References

[1] Iverson, R.M. The physics of debris flows. *Reviews of Geophysics* 35(3) (1997), pp.245–296.

[2] Iverson, R.M., The debris-flow rheology myth. In: Rickenmann D, Chen CL (eds.): *Debris-Flow Hazards Mitigation: Mechanics, Prediction, and Assessment*; Proceedings of the 3rd International DFHM Conference Davos Switzerland September 10-12 2003, Millpress, Rotterdam, pp. 303–314, 2003.

[3] Ancey, C., Debris Flows and Related Phenomena. In: Balmforth, N.J.; Provenzale, A. (eds): *Geomorphological Fluid Mechanics*. Lecture Notes in Physics (LNP) 582, pp. 528–547, (2001).

[4] Zhang S., Hong Y., Yu B., Detecting infrasound emission of debris flow for warning purpose, *10 Congress Interpraevent*, pp. 359–364, 2004.

[5] Bedard A.J., Detection of avalanches using atmospheric infrasound, Proceedings; *Western Snow Conference*, Fort Collins, CO, 1989.

[6] Bedard A.J., An evaluation of atmospheric infrasound for monitoring avalanches, Proceedings; *7th International Symposium on Acoustic Sensing*

and Associated Techniques of the Atmosphere and Oceans, Boulder, CO, 1994.

[7] Bedard A.J., Infrasonic and near infrasonic atmospheric sounding and imaging, NOAA/EARL/Environmental Technology Laboratory, 1996.

[8] Scott E.D., Lance C., Infrasonic monitoring of avalanche activity, Proceedings; International Snow Science Workshop, Penticton, British Columbia, 2002.

[9] Scott E.D., Results of recent infrasound avalanche monitoring studies, Proceedings; International Snow Science Workshop, Jackson Hole, Wyoming, 2004.

[10] Scott E.D., Practical implementation of avalanche infrasound monitoring technology for operational utilization near Teton Pass Wyoming, Proceedings; International Snow Science Workshop, 2006.

[11] Christie D. R., Vivas Veloso J. A., Campus P., Bell M., Hoffmann T., Langlois A., Martysevich P., Demirovic E., Carvalho J., Detection of atmospheric nuclear explosions : the infrasound component of the International monitoring system, Journal Kerntechnik, Monitoring the Nuclear-Test-Ban, vol. 66, no 3 (20 ref.), pp. 96–101, 2001.

[12] Okuda S., Okunishi K., Suwa H., Observation of debris flow at Kamikamihori Valley of Mt. Yakedade, Excursion Guidebook of the Third Meeting of IGU commission on Field Experiment in Geomorphology, pp127–130, 1980.

[13] Wu J., Kang Z., Tian L., Zhang S., Observation and investigation of debris flows at Jiangjia Gully in Yunnan Province (China), Sci. Press, Beijing, 1990.

[14] Hadley K., Lahusen R., Deployment of an acoustic flow monitor system and examples of its application at Mount Pinatubo, Philippines (abstract), Eos Trans. AGU, 72(44), F67, 1991.

[15] Marchi L., Arattano M., Deganutti A., Ten years of debris-flow monitoring in the Moscardo Torrent (Italian Alps), Geomorphology, 46(1-2), 1-17, 2002.

[16] Arattano M., Monitoring the presence of the debris-flow front and its velocity through ground vibrations detectors, Proceedings of the Third International Conference on Debris-Flow Hazards Mitigation: Mechanics, Prediction and Assessment, Millpress, Rotterdam, Vol.2, pp731–743, 2003.

[17] Huang, C.-J., H.-Y. Yin, C.-Y. Chen, C.-H. Yeh, And C.-L. Wang, Ground Vibrations produced by rock motions and debris flow, J. Geophys. Res., 112, F02014, doi:10.1029/2005JF000437, 2007.

[18] Chou H.T., Cheung Y.L., Zhang S. C., Calibration of infrasound monitoring systems and acoustic characteristics of debris-flow movements by field studies, Institute of Mountain Hazards and Environment, Chinese Academy of Science and Ministry of Water resources, 2007.

[19] Takahasi T., Debris Flow, International association for hydraulic research (IAHR),1991.

[20] Percival D.B., Walden A.T., Spectral Analysis for Physical Applications, Cambridge Academic Press, 1998.

[21] Smith S. W., The Scientist and Engineers Guide to Digital Signal Processing, *California Technical Publishing*, 1997.

[22] Grosse C, Ruck Hj, Bahr G., Analyse von Schallemissionssignalen unter Verwendung der Wavelet-Transformation 13. Kolloquium Schallemission, Jena 2001

[23] Eric D. Ryan, Joel T. Cramer, Alison D. Egan, Michael J. Hartman and Trent J., A real-time earthquake detector with prefiltering by wavelets *Computers & Geosciences*, Volume 29, Issue 7, pp. 911–919, 2003.

[24] F. Botella, J. Rosa-Herranz, J. J. Giner, S. Molina and J., Time and frequency domain responses of the mechanomyogram and electromyogram during isometric ramp contractions: A comparison of the short-time Fourier and continuous wavelet transforms, *Journal of Electromyography and Kinesiology*, Volume 18, Issue 1, Pages 54–67, 2003.

Determination of effective antecedent rainfall for debris flow forecast based on soil moisture content observation in Jiangjia Gully, China

F. Wei[1,2], K. Hu[2], J. Zhang[2], Y. Jiang[2] & J. Chen[3]
[1]Key Laboratory of Mountain Hazards and Surface Process,
Chinese Academy of Science, Chengdu, China
[2]Institute of Mountain Hazards and Environment,
Chinese Academy of Sciences, Chengdu, China
[3]School of Geographical Sciences, Southwest University, Chongqing,
China

Abstract

Effective antecedent rainfall (EAR), one of important factors for debris flow forecast, has different ways of influencing debris flow initiation for different types of debris flows. For soil-mechanics-typed debris flow, EAR impacts its initiation by changing the soil moisture content, and for hydromechanics-typed debris flow, EAR impacts its initiation by increasing the surface runoff. For this reason, the methods of determining EAR for different types of debris flows are different. The method for the former type of debris flow is discussed in this paper. Under the assumptions that soil moisture content due to antecedent rainfall decays in the same way as EAR, and that the decays for different events are mutually independent, the variation of EAR can be carried out through analyzing the variation of soil moisture content. The EAR for debris flow forecast can then be determined. The decaying of soil moisture content had been analyzed according to the field observation of rainfall and soil moisture content in Jiangjia Gully in Yunan Province, where debris flows are caused by soil mechanical changing triggered by rainfall. Based on the field observation and data analysis, the formula of calculating EAR for Jiangjia Gully is made out with least-squares procedure.
Keywords: debris flow, forecast, antecedent rainfall, effective rainfall, soil moisture content.

WIT Transactions on Engineering Sciences, Vol 60, © 2008 WIT Press
www.witpress.com, ISSN 1743-3533 (on-line)
doi:10.2495/DEB080021

1 Introduction

Rainfall is an important factor of rainfall-typed debris flow forecast because it is the direct triggering factor of debris flow initiation. In a debris flow event, the rainfall impacting its initiation includes antecedent rainfall and current rainfall. The former consists of effective antecedent rainfall (EAR) which influences the event and loss of rainfall which is lost through surface runoff, groundwater runoff and evaporation etc. The latter consists of effective current rainfall (ECR) which is the part of rainfall before the event and surplus rainfall which is the part of rainfall after the event. Both EAR and ECR are the important factors of debris flow forecast because they impact debris flow initiation jointly. ECR can be obtained through rainfall forecast and rainfall monitoring, but it's difficult to calculate or evaluate EAR, and there is no reliable approach at present. In past researches, Senoo et al (1985) gave an equation to calculate EAR as $R_a = \sum_{t=1}^{14} a_t R_t$,

where R_a is EAR, R_t is the daily-rainfall on the t-day before, $a_t = 0.5^{\frac{1}{T}}$ is decrement rate, where T is the half life of rainfall. Rainfall in the last 14 days is considered in this equation [1]. This equation was used widely in Japan and was modified in later applications (such as Fujii et al. [3]; Kubota et al. [2]; Hayashi et al. [4] and Senoo et al. [5]), but the form of the equation was not changed [2–6]. Tan [6] adopted monthly rainfall as antecedent rainfall in the research on the character of rainfall vertical distribution and critical rainfall of debris flow forecast in Babuli Gully, Sichuan Province, China and employed the equation of Senoo (1985) in other research (1989) [7–8]. The equation $P_{a0} = P_1 K + P_2 K^2 + P_3 K^3 + ... + P_n K^n$ was used by Chen [9] to calculate EAR in debris flow forecast, where P_{a0} is EAR, P_1, P_2, P_3, P_n are the rainfall respectively on the 1st, 2nd, n[th] day past, K is the decrease coefficient. In this equation, K is suggested from 0.8 to 0.9, and $n =20$. Tan et al. [8] considered the action of antecedent rainfall in his research of debris flow forecast for railway. But no equation was given out, only a coefficient K (≥ 1) was used to correct the rainfall. Fan el at [10] used a recession coefficient α to express EAR in the research on critical threshold rainfall of debris flow occurrence in central Taiwan and adopted Fedora's (1989) recession coefficient of antecedent precipitation $k = 0.881 + 0.00793 \times \ln(a)$ in the research of storm runoff to determine $\alpha = \sqrt{k}$, where α is the catchment area [11,12]. According to these researches, two parameters are difficult to determine in calculating EAR: the decay coefficient and the number of days. Furthermore, all rainfalls that occurred in a certain period have been considered, although some light rainfalls may be lost completely. It seems just for the reason that the EAR is difficult to determine or evaluate accurately, the EAR has been not considered in many researches of debris flow forecast. However, it's a very important factor impacting debris flow initiation, it can't be neglected in debris flow forecast. In order to resolve this problem, the decay process of EAR has to be researched.

According to the field observation and the research of Wu [13], the initiation of debris flow can be classified into two types. One is soil-mechanics-typed that the soil on the slope becomes unstable and forms debris flow while rainfall increases the soil moisture content and changes the characteristics of soil mechanics. And the other one is hydromechanics-typed that debris on slope or valley beds is eroded by increasing runoff and then forms debris flow. For the former, EAR should be researched through analyzing the decaying of soil moisture content after rainfall, and for the latter, it should be researched through analyzing the decaying of runoff after rainfall. The decaying of runoff has been researched largely in hydrology, and some results of them can be used in determining EAR for hydromechanics-typed debris flow forecast. The method of determining EAR discussed in this paper is for the soil-mechanics-typed debris flow forecast. It is researched through observing the rainfall and soil moisture content in Jiangjia Gully in the province of Yunnan, China (Fig. 1), where debris flows are caused by soil mechanics changing triggered by rainfall, and where Dongchuan Debris flow Observation Station, Chinese Academy of Sciences is located.

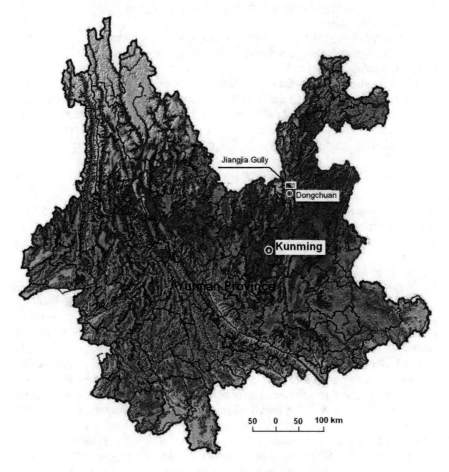

Figure 1:   The position of Jiangjia Gully.

2 Relation between EAR and variation of soil moisture content

For soil-mechanics-typed debris flow, soil moisture content is crucial for debris flow initiation, and the increase of soil moisture content is caused by rainfall. So the soil moisture content and rainfall are closely related. The soil moisture content increases rapidly during rainfall but decreases rapidly after the rainfall for runoff and evaporation, etc. The rapid decrease of soil moisture content causes its action on debris flow initiation to weaken fast. Because the soil moisture content is caused by rainfall, it means the impact of antecedent rainfall on debris flow initiation weakens rapidly. In other words, its EAR decreases rapidly. Therefore it can be assumed that the decrease of EAR coincides with the decrease of soil moisture content and decays in the same manner. Under this assumption, decaying of EAR can be determined through analyzing the decaying of soil moisture content.

Of course, more rainfall events may happen while the effective rainfall of the former event doesn't lose completely. It will induce superimposing of EAR from different rainfall events, as does the soil moisture content. In order to make it simple, it can be assumed that the decrease processes of EAR of different events are mutually independent, and that the decrease processes of soil moisture contents due to different rainfalls events are also mutually independent. Under this assumption, the total antecedent effective rainfall is the linear superimposing of the effective rainfall of every rainfall event, so dose the total soil moisture content.

$$EF=EF_1+EF_2+...+EF_n \tag{1}$$
$$EW=EW_1+EW_2+...+EW_n+c \tag{2}$$

Where EF and EW are total EAR and total soil moisture content, EF_n and EW_n are the effective rainfall and soil moisture content of the rainfall event on the n-day before, c is a constant.

Generally soil moisture content increases along with the increase of rainfall. However, it is not a strict increase because same precipitations with different intensities and processes may cause different infiltrations and induce different soil moisture contents. In order to simplify it, it is assumed that in the 24-hour statistics period that soil moisture content increases linearly with the increase of rainfall. Furthermore, the increase of soil moisture content is zero while the rainfall is zero. So the relation between EAR and the soil moisture content is reduced to a simple coefficient relation. Set the effective rainfall of the rainfall event on the i-day before $EF_i=f(F, i)$, where F is the rainfall on the i-day before, and the soil moisture content due to the rainfall event on the i-day before $EW_i=f(W, i)$, where W is the increase of soil moisture content due to the rainfall on the i-day before, then $f(F, i)$ and $g(W, i)$ should have the same functional form based on the assumption that the decaying of soil moisture content and effective rainfall follow the same manner of decaying. Thus, the difficult problem of determining antecedent effective rainfall is transformed to the problem of determining soil moisture content, which can be resolved by field observation and statistics analysis.

3 Observation of rainfall and soil moisture content

In order to determine the decay process of soil moisture content after rainfall and the functional form of $g(W,i)$, the rainfall and soil moisture content were observed for 39 days continuously in field in the rainy season of 2003.

The period of observation is from 30 July to 6 September. The position of observation is in Jiangjia Gully, Yunnan Province, China. Most of the debris flows in this catchment are soil-mechanics-typed. The debris flows events appear about 15 times per year averagely triggered by rainfall. There are good observation conditions here because the Dongchuan Debris Flow Observation Station, Chinese Academy of Sciences is located in this catchment. Three points with different characters were selected to observe the rainfall and soil moisture content (Fig. 2). The first point is on a semi-naked slope with 31° gradient and

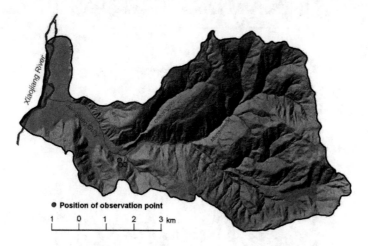

Figure 2:   The catchment of Jiangjia Gully and position of the observation points.

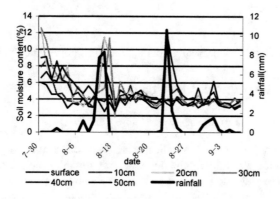

Figure 3:   Observation data in the first observation point.

NE25° aspect. The second point is on a forest slope with 40° gradient and NE20°. The third point is on naked flat ground. A profile with 50cm depth was made to observe the soil moisture content in different depth (surface, 10cm, 20cm, 30cm, 40cm and 50cm) in every observation point.

The observation data of rainfall and soil moisture content on 3 observation points are illustrated in Fig. 3 to Fig. 5.

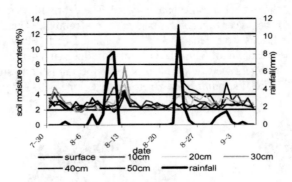

Figure 4:   Observation data in the second observation point.

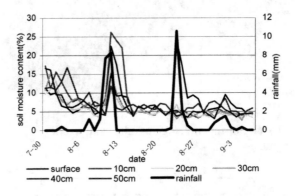

Figure 5:   Observation data in the third observation point.

4   Data analysis and EAR determination

4.1 Observation data analysis

The data illustrated in figure 3–5 indicate that the soil moisture content increased rapidly on the day with rainfall and decreased rapidly after the rainfall and kept a relatively stable value about one week later. The same tendency of soil moisture content decay appears in different observation points with different conditions and different depth of these profiles. In these observation points, the conditions of the first observation point are most similar to the source region of debris flow in Jiangjia Gully where debris flow forms from steep slopes while the soil on the slope becomes unstable under the triggering of rainfall. Furthermore, debris flow forms from the shallow soil saturated by rainfall on the slope according to the research of Cui et al (2003) and the field observation. The data of the 20cm depth of the first observation point are selected as the typical data to be analyzed.

According to the data analysis, following conclusions about the decay process of soil moisture content can be deduced:

(1)   The soil moisture content has a relatively stable value although there is no rainfall in a long period. This value can be considered as the basic soil moisture content without relation to any specific rainfall event. So this value can be set to a constant c not included in EW_i.

(2) $EW_i=W$ while $i=0$ and $EW_i=0$ while $W=0$.

(3) EW_i should be the monotonic decreasing function of i and monotonic increasing function of W.

(4) EW_i decreases very rapidly while i increasing and should be convergent while it is summed from 0 to ∞.

Based on these conclusions, $EW_i=g(W,i)$ can be assumed as:

$$EW_i = W \times \frac{i + a^k}{(i + a)^k} \tag{3}$$

Where a and k are constants. Then the total soil moisture content EW is:

$$EW = EW_1 + EW_2 + \cdots + EW_n + c = \sum_{i=1}^{n} W \times \frac{i + a^k}{(i + a)^k} + c \tag{4}$$

Because there is no rainfall for a long period before 10 August and from 11 August to 22 August, the process of soil moisture content decreasing can be considered independently. So the observation data from 10 to 22 August are selected to fit equation (4) with least-squares procedure. In the fitting, k is set to 3, 4 and 5 separately because k must be more than 2 in order to make equation (4) convergent. The fitting results indicate 3 is best for k, and when $k=3$, $a=0.08$, $c=4.02$. Then

$$EW_i = W \times \frac{i + 0.08^3}{(i + 0.08)^3} \tag{5}$$

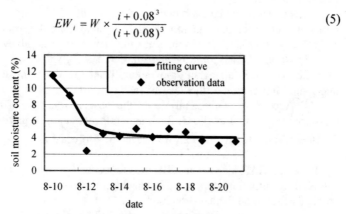

Figure 6:   Comparison of fitting curve and observation data.

The confidence interval of the fitting under 95% credence of a and c are $(-0.02746, 0.1868)$ and $(3.565, 4.479)$, and the error of mean square root is 0.618. The fitting curve and the observation data are shown in figure 6.

4.2 Determination of EAR

According to the analysis on the relation between the decay processes of soil moisture content and EAR, $EF_i=f(F, i)$ and $EW_i=g(W, i)$ have same functional form. According to equation (5), the effective rainfall of the rainfall event on the i-day before can be expressed as:

$$EF_i = F \times \frac{i + 0.08^3}{(i + 0.08)^3} \tag{6}$$

Under the assumption that the decrease of EAR of different rainfall events is mutually independent and according to equation (1), the total EAR is expressed as:

$$EF = \sum_{i=1}^{n} F \times \frac{i + 0.08^3}{(i + 0.08)^3} \tag{7}$$

Although equation (7) is convergent, in order to make the calculation simple, the effective rainfall of some rainfall events can be neglected while it decreases to less than 0.1mm. If ten such events are neglected, the neglected effective rainfall amount is only 1mm and this value has almost no influence on the result of debris flow forecast which is set up based on statistics approach. The span of n becomes limited under this simplification and the calculation is simplified in practice.

5 Conclusions and discussion

The following conclusions are drawn from the analysis of field observation data as well as the model of determining EAR.

(1) EAR impacts the initiation of debris flow and is an important factor for debris flow forecast.

(2) For soil-mechanics-typed debris flow, the EAR impacting debris flow initiation can be reflected in soil moisture content. And the soil moisture content and effective rainfall decay in the same manner after a rainfall event.

(3) Under the assumption that the decrease processes of effective rainfall from different rainfall events are mutually independent, the total EAR is the linear superimposition of the EAR of each rainfall event.

(4) According to the analysis on the observation data of rainfall and soil moisture content in Jiangjia Gully, Yunnan Province, the equation of calculating the antecedent effective rainfall for debris flow forecast is $EF = \sum_{i=1}^{n} F \times \frac{i + 0.08^3}{(i + 0.08)^3}$.

However, EAR decays in different forms and brings different impacts on debris flow initiation depending upon environment conditions. The following problems should be further discussed.

(1) For soil-mechanics-typed debris flow, EAR impacts debris flow initiation through changing the soil moisture content, and for hydromechanics-typed debris

flow, it impacts debris flow initiation through changing the runoff. However, only the former is discussed in this paper. The latter should be discussed in later research, and a more general formula for both types of debris flows is needed to supply a simple approach of determining EAR for debris flow forecast.

(2) Regional difference is important for determining EAR because the decay process of soil moisture content is influenced by many factors such as climate, vegetation, soil, geomorphology etc. However, study in this paper is carried out based on observations in a given catchment, Jiangjia Gully, the application of the EAR formula must be limited to regions with similar natural conditions. In order to satisfy the requirement of debris flow forecast in different regions, formulas for different regions have to be set up by more observations in later research.

Acknowledgement

This research is supported by the Knowledge Innovation Program of Chinese Academy of Sciences (KZCX3-SW-352).

References

[1] Senoo, K. et al. Rainfall indexes for debris flow warning evacuating program. *Shin-Sabo*, 1985, 38(2):16–21. (in Japanese)

[2] Kubota, T. et al. A study on a Neural Network system for critical rainfall determination of debris flow warning and Evacuation. *Journal of the Japan Society of Erosion Control Engineering*, 1995, 47(6): 8–14. (in Japanese)

[3] Fujii, K. et al. Study on the Accuracy of warning and evacuation timing for debris flow. *Journal of the Japan Society of Erosion Control Engineering*, 1994, 47(2): 35–42. (in Japanese)

[4] Hayashi, T. et al. Nobutomo Osanai. Study on the management of critical rainfall determination of debris flow warning. *Journal of the Japan Society of Erosion Control Engineering*, 2000, 53(2): 57–61. (in Japanese)

[5] Senoo, K. et al. On the theme and improvement of standard rainfall of warning and evacuation from sediment disasters. *Journal of the Japan Society of Erosion Control Engineering*, 2001, 53(6): 37–44. (in Japanese)

[6] Tan, W. The character of rainfall vertical distribution and critical rainfall of debris flow forecast in Babuli Gully. *Sichuan Meteorology* (in Chinese), 1988, 8(2): 25–28.

[7] Tan, W. Distribution characters of critical rainfall line for the debris flow gully. *Bulletin of Water and Soil Conservation*, 1989, 9(6): 21–26. (in Chinese)

[8] Tan, B. et al. Study on prediction for rainstorm debris flow along mountain district railways. *Journal of Natural Disasters*, 1995, 4(2): 43–52. (in Chinese)

[9] Chen, J. Study on debris flow forecast in Jiangjia Gully. *In: Observation and Research on Debris Flows in Jiangjia Gully in Yunnan(ed. Wu, J., Kang, Z. et al), Beijing: Science Press*, 1990, 197–213. (in Chinese)

[10] Fan, J. C. et al. Determination of critical thresholds for debris-flow occurrence in central Taiwan and their revision after the 1999 Chi-Chi great earthquake. *In: Debris Flow Hazard Mitigation: Mechanics, Prediction, and Assessment (ed. Rickenmann, D. and Chen, C. L.), Proceedings 3rd International DFHM Conference, Davos, Switzerland, September 10-12, Rotterdam: Millpress,* 2003, 103–114.

[11] Fedora, M. A. et al. Storm runoff simulation using an antecedent precipitation index(API) model . *Journal of hydrology,* 1989, 112:121–133.

[12] Wu, J. et al. Debris flow and its prevention (in Chinese). *Beijing: Science Press,* 1993, 81–89.

[13] Cui, P. et al. Relationship between occurrence of debris flow and antecedent precipitation: taking the Jiangjia Gulley as an Example. *Science of Soil and Water Conservation,* 2003, 1(1): 11–15. (in Chinese)

Debris flow mitigation with flexible ring net barriers – field tests and case studies

C. Wendeler[1], B. W. McArdell[1], A. Volkwein[1], M. Denk[2]
& E. Gröner[2]
[1]*WSL Swiss Federal Research Institute, Switzerland*
[2]*Geobrugg AG Protection Systems, Switzerland*

Abstract

A new type of debris flow mitigation measure, flexible ring-net barrier systems, are cost-effective and efficient compared to massive concrete barriers. However, the performance of these systems has not yet been investigated systematically. For this reason a wire ring-net barrier system has been installed in the Illgraben torrent, to investigate its performance, measure the forces and to provide information on the expected maintenance. Additionally, this net-testing facility allows for optimization of the structure and provides a basis for design guidelines. This paper describes the measurement facilities at the barrier and the debris flow events of 2006. First results of the filling event and their interpretation with the computational model are discussed.
Keywords: debris flow mitigation, flexible debris flow barriers, numerical simulation, field testing.

1   Introduction

Debris flows are initialised mostly by heavy rainfalls where the water quickly infiltrates into and mobilizes the ground material in mountainous regions. They flow downwards in riverbeds and along slopes, carrying large blocks and boulders, and endanger humans and their infrastructure. To reduce debris flow damage adequate protection measures have to be chosen. In regions where large debris flows occur frequently the best protection measures are typically large dams to re-route the debris to less vulnerable areas or special retention basins. But for smaller volumes a new protection system, the flexible ring-net barrier (Fig. 1), is now in a testing and developing phase in Switzerland. As shown here,

WIT Transactions on Engineering Sciences, Vol 60, © 2008 WIT Press
www.witpress.com, ISSN 1743-3533 (on-line)
doi:10.2495/DEB080031

Figure 1:   Debris flow deposit directly in front of a building and a filled flexible barrier system.

it can ideally be used to span the cross section of a river bed to stop the expected debris flow volume and to drain the material.

First tests with such ring-net barriers were carried out at the United States Geological Survey (USGS) Debris Flow Flume in 1996 [1] where the peak measured loads in the ropes were 40 kN and 10 m^3 of debris were retained. Motivated by these tests, the Swiss Federal Research Institute WSL built a full-scale test site in a very active debris flow channel in Switzerland.

One advantage of ring-net barriers in comparison to traditional concrete structures is that the ring-net barriers are light and flexible and can easily be installed in remote regions by transporting the system with helicopters. Furthermore, the maximum impact forces are reduced by long braking distances and flexible deforming structures. The stopping process has already been studied using similar barriers intended as protection against rockfall, woody debris in rivers or small snow slides. However, the load distribution over the barrier for debris flows is different than other applications. So, corresponding research is necessary, and a new project was initiated in 2005 that combines the results from full-scale field tests and laboratory experiments with numerical simulation results, giving new insight into the flow barrier interaction during and after a debris flow impact.

2   Test site description

In 2005, the first barrier system was installed at the Illgraben, one of the most active debris flow torrents in the Swiss Alps. The annual average debris flows occurring in the Illgraben lies between 4-6 events per season. Additionally, the torrent has been monitored by the WSL since 2000 and is equipped with geophones to measure the front travel time, laser, radar, and ultrasonic devices for the flow height, and a flow force plate to continuously record normal and shear forces, which together with the flow depth allows calculation of the bulk density of the flow [2].

3 Barrier details

There are two different set-ups of the barriers depending on the shape of the torrent (Fig. 2). For wide U-shaped channel cross sections, the so-called U-Barrier system was developed with posts in the middle of the construction transferring the loads to the banks. For narrower V-shaped channels up to 12-15 m wide a so-called V-Barrier without any posts is sufficient. The standard construction height of these barriers is around 3-6 m.

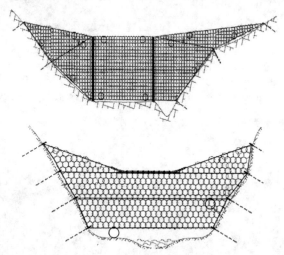

Figure 2:   U (top) and V-barrier system (bottom) against debris flow.

In both systems, a wire ring-net is mounted between the horizontal steel wire ropes that are anchored in both sides of the channel side slopes. Its function is to transport the area loads to the ropes where a part of the energy is absorbed by elongation of the so-called brake rings (see Fig. 3) installed in the ropes as a peak-force damping system. Loads up to 400 kN can be carried and transferred to the anchors.

The test barrier system (Fig. 4) has been instrumented to measure the interaction of the flow with the barrier. Above the barrier, a laser device measures the flow height. On the right channel bank a video camera documents the debris flow events and their interaction with the barrier. At night, a flood light on the left channel side produces the additional illumination. To measure tension forces in the support ropes, load cells with a range up to 500 kN are installed at the ends of the ropes. The system is triggered by a geophone installed upstream. The data are transferred to the WSL via a wireless data modem.

A newly designed test barrier was installed in late April 2006 in the torrent within a one week period (including earthworks to prepare the river bed at the barrier location) before the start of the debris flow season to avoid construction interruptions due to debris flows. The main difference to the barrier system of 2005 [3] is a change within the net panel from two support ropes and additional brake elements installed between the ring net and lateral anchors.

Figure 3:   A not deformed brake ring (left) compared with an elongated one (right) installed in support ropes: A rope passes through a hollow steel tube bent into a ring form. Once the rope is loaded, the ring diameter narrows plastically thereby absorbing energy.

Figure 4:   Construction phase and final set up of the barrier 2006.

4 Field results

Four weeks after installation, on May 18, the barrier captured the front of a debris flow and – after filling – was overtopped by subsequent flows, providing a chance to evaluate the behaviour under severe field conditions. Another five debris flows passed over the barrier during 2006 (Table 1). The two events in June were the largest ones by the total flow volume but considering the densities, the more powerful events were the events on July 28, and the one in October with densities larger than 2000 kg/m^3. The retained debris volume is 1000 m^3, calculated from survey measurements, before and after the filling event (Fig. 5). The filling event itself, with a velocity of 2.9 m/s and a bulk density value of about 1600 kg/m^3, was a muddy or watery debris flow. The low density of the filling debris flow partially explains the longer than normal filling time (more than 1 minute). The interaction with the barrier therefore was not as intense as it would have been for a granular debris flow, which typically occurs over a few seconds.

Table 1:   Overview of the debris flow events in 2006 at the Illgraben [6].

Date	Volume	Density	Flow height	Front velocity	Front shape
	m^3	kg/m^3	m	m/s	
18 May	15,000	1620	1.4	2.9	Watery
24 June	50,000	1520	3.2	4.8	Granular
		1320			Watery
27 June	70,000	(~1800)	2.5	3.9	(granular body)
18 July	50,000	1600	2.5	4.8	Watery
28 July	10,000	2130	1.4	2.0	Granular
3 October	10,000	2060	1.4	1.65	Granular

Figure 5:   Measured profile of the Illgraben torrent close to the test barrier before and after the filling event.

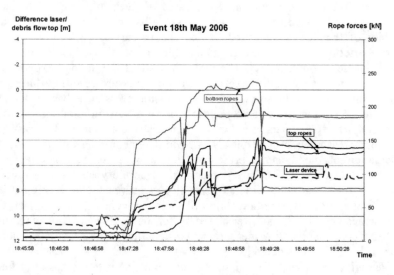

Figure 6:   Tension forces in the load cells on May 18, 2006.

The tension forces in the support ropes during the filling event are shown in Fig. 6. The maximum load level of the bottom support ropes is around 240 kN each during the filling process. The top support ropes were loaded less, at 150 kN each. These values add to the existing data obtained earlier in field and laboratory tests [1, 3, 4]. This collection enables comparison and analysis [5].

5 Discussion

Ropes forces: One important observation of the filling process was that the bottom ropes are more loaded than the top ropes. The opening of the barrier at the river bed was around half a meter in height and so that small floods may pass beneath the barrier. During the subsequent overtopping phase it is reversed: then the top support ropes are directly influenced by the overflowing debris flow and are loaded more than the bottom support ropes. In every load curve of support ropes in Fig. 6, sudden losses of the rope forces are visible. This is caused by the elongation of the brake rings.

Load model: First guidelines for design of these flexible barrier systems are given in [7] based on an empirical design method by [8]. These formulas, based on conservation of energy, calculate the stopped volume and the discharge of the flow and work fine for granular flows. However, the filling process for mudflow streams (as on May 18th) isn't adequately modelled. Therefore a new calculation method has to be developed.

A first approach assumes that a muddy debris flow has a flow regime similar to a turbulent flood water event. Therefore, more the passing of the liquid phase and only some bigger boulders impacting the net comprise the load, compared to a dynamic impact of a larger-density debris flow filling up the barrier very rapidly. The pressure exerted on obstacles by a turbulent muddy debris flow then depends on flow velocity and the obstacle's front area and shape.

An overview of the calculated pressures is given in Table 2. The static pressure is calculated as active earth pressure based on Coulomb [9] with a density of the debris deposited behind the barrier of 2300 kg/m^3 and an inertial friction angle of 35°. Estimates for the basal friction angle can be found in McArdell et al. [2]. The table shows that the method explained in [7] results in a very high maximum dynamic pressure resulting due to the long filling time. In the second row the dynamic pressure is back-calculated iteratively from the measured rope forces using a Newton iteration according to a simplified rope analysis for uniform distributed loads. The resulting dynamic pressure is around 60 kN/m^2. Similar magnitude estimates by the calculation of the dynamic pressure using a dynamic overload factor of $P_{dyn}/P_{stat} = 2.2$ obtained from corresponding laboratory tests [10] shown in the third row. Ongoing additional resistance measurements of a ring-net in a clear water flow (no sediments) will help to consolidate the last two approaches and identify a lower boundary for the load level. The comparison with different debris flow measurements including solid structural concrete measures will be considered [5].

Numerical modelling: Once a model for the acting pressure has been found the results can be used in a corresponding numerical simulation tool that enables development of further barriers. The simulations are carried out with the finite element software FARO [11] based on a discrete element formulation. The software has been developed for the calculation of flexible rock fall barriers where the dynamic acting force of the impacting boulder induces large deformation in the entire system necessitating non-linear simulation methods. The software now has been modified to also account for forces induces by a debris flow. Figure 7 shows a simulated barrier together with the filled Illgraben barrier for an applied acting pressure according to Rickenmann [8]. The forces were applied quasi-statically.

Table 2:   Pressure values on the barrier.

	Velocity	Velocity head	Obstacle area	Static pressure	Max. pressure
	m/s	kg/ms^2	m^2	kN/m^2	kN/m^2
Energy conservation [8]	2.9	6730	10.1	21.7	780.0
Back calculated from measured rope forces	2.9	6730	10.1	21.7	59.4
Dynamic factor = 2.2 from laboratory tests	2.9	6730	10.1	21.7	47.8

Table 3:   Comparison of simulation results with measured field data.

Support ropes	Simulated forces	Measured field forces	Deviation
	kN	kN	%
Top	160	150	6
Bottom	210	248	15

Figure 7:   Finite element model of the test barrier compared to the deformed field barrier.

Both the forces in the ropes (Table 3) and the deformations correspond well to the field observations. The actual load application first calculates the mass to be stopped and the resulting total kinetic energy that has to be absorbed using the energy conservation approach described above. Together with an estimated braking distance this results in a total brake force that is equally distributed on the single element nodes of the finite element model. The node loads increase over the time as the barrier is progressively filled.

6 Case study

Multilevel debris flow barrier Milibach, Hasliberg, Bernese Oberland / Switzerland

Floods and a debris flow event occurred in the Milibach on 22. August 2005 which resulted in serious debris coverage and damage in the Weiler Reuti / Hasliberg and in Meiringen. The Milibach above Reuti comprises two part creeks, the Lauenenbach being situated in the upper catchment area in the Alenienschiefer (schist). Due to heavy rainfalls, within about 1 hour a total of approximately 13'000 m^3 of loose soil material became detached and flowed downhill as a mudflow in 2 to 3 surges (muddy debris flow, rich in fine material).

On the way to the valley, additional soil material was eroded from the riverlet, resulting in a much greater event in Meiringen than the original volume.

For the upper drainage area of the Lauenenbach ("Gummen"), provision has been made for the debris flow to be held back during a future event (return period 30 years) by means of 13 flexible, debris flow barrier systems installed in series (Fig. 8). These are arranged and dimensioned to provide sufficient retention volumes and are also capable of bearing the expected debris flow impact and overflow loads, as well as snow and static loads.

Figure 8: Barrier under construction at Gummen (left). Two barriers already installed (right).

7 Conclusion

The Illgraben torrent observation station is ideal to test flexible net barriers under natural conditions due to the relatively frequent occurrence of large debris flows. First testing phases 2005 and 2006 revealed good results to help in the proper design and improvement of these systems. An improved barrier set up will be installed in spring 2007 to further optimise the design. First load approaches and back calculations already show promising results for further developments.

Acknowledgements

We thank Bruno Fritschi for his careful and competent design of the Illgraben observation station and instrumentation for the barrier. We are grateful to Francois Dufour, Alexandre Badoux, and Christoph Graf for their daily support within this project.

References

[1]   DeNatale, J. S., Iverson, R. M., Major, J. J., LaHusen R.G., Fliegel, G. L., Duffy, J. D. 1999. Experimental Testing of flexible barriers for containment of debris flows, *Open-File Report* 99-205, U.S. Geological Survey.
[2]   McArdell, B. W., Bartelt, P. & Kowalski, J. 2007. Field observations of basal forces and fluid pore pressure in a debris flow. *Geophysical Research Letters*, 34 (LO7406), doi:10.1029/2006GL029183.
[3]   Wendeler, C., McArdell, B. W., Rickenmann, D., Volkwein, A., Roth, A., Denk, M. 2006. Field testing and numerical modelling of flexible debris flow barriers, *Proc. Int. Conf. on Physical Modelling in Geotechnics*, Hong Kong.
[4]   DeNatale, J. S., Fiegel, G. L., Iverson R. M., Major J. J., LaHusen, R. G., Duffy, J.D. & Fisher, G. D.. 1997. Response of flexible wire rope barriers to debris flows loading. *Proc. 1st.International Conference on DFHM*, ASCE, San Francisco, pp 616–625.
[5]   Wendeler, C. In preparation. *Field investigations and modeling of the interaction of debris flows with flexible ring-net barriers.* Doctoral dissertation, ETH Zurich, Switzerland.
[6]   McArdell, B. W., Wendeler, C., Roth, A., Kalejta, J., Rorem, E. 2007. Field observations of the interaction of debris flows with flexible barriers, *First North American Landslide Conference*, Vail.
[7]   Roth, A., Kästli, A. & Frenez, Th. 2004. Debris Flow Mitigation by Means of Flexible Barriers, *Proc. Int. Symp. Interpraevent.* Riva del Garda, Italy. Klagenfurt: Interpraevent.
[8]   Rickenmann, D. 1999. Empirical relationships for debris flows. *Natural Hazards.* 19(1): 47–77.
[9]   Gudehus, G. 1981. *Bodenmechanik.* Ferdinant Enke Verlag, Stuttgart.
[10] Wendeler C., B.W. McArdell, D. Rickenmann, A. Volkwein, A. Roth & M. Denk. 2005. Testing and numerical modeling of flexible debris flow barriers, in Ng, Zhang & Wang (Eds), Physical Modeling in Geotechnics – 6th ICPMG '06, Balkema.
[11] Volkwein A. 2005. Numerical Simulation of flexible rockfall protection systems, *Proc. Computing in Civil Engineering.* Cancun: ASCE.

Distribution of aerial hazard maps of debris flow on a social network service

T. Moriyama[1], H. Nakayama[2], K. Kon[3], M. Hirano[4] & M. Hikida[5]
[1]Department of EcoDesign, Sojo University, Japan
[2]Siesta Club Co. Ltd., Japan
[3]NPO Tanoshii Mogura Club, Japan
[4]NPO Disaster Prevention Network Research Institute, Japan
[5]Dept. of Civil Engineering, Kagoshima College of Technology, Japan

Abstract

Disaster prevention information systems should maintain high levels of reliability for information. Internet Bulletin Board Systems (BBS) occasionally include inaccurate, malicious or incorrect information. Anonymous posts to bulletin boards are particularly unreliable. BBS should not serve as primary means for official communication. Moreover, most local governments are hesitant to issue evacuation orders despite the urgency of timely announcements because of the suddenness of debris flows. In the current study, we developed a disaster prevention information system using a combined Geographic Information System (GIS) and Social Network Service (SNS) called giSight. The function of SNS is to keep the reliability of information at a high level by registering users. A hazard map of landslide and debris flow is indicated on the GIS with high-resolution aerial photograph tile maps. This hazard map identifies the mesh polygon with dangerous conditions in real-time, *i.e.* dynamically. This system is not only useful for disaster prevention, but is also expected to facilitate the exchange of information by residents in normal circumstances.

Keywords: debris flow, hazard map, critical rainfall, social network service, disaster information system, Geographic Information System.

1 Introduction

Evacuation of residents is occasionally necessary to prevent the loss of life from debris flow following intense rainfall. However, official evacuation orders by

 WIT Transactions on Engineering Sciences, Vol 60, © 2008 WIT Press
www.witpress.com, ISSN 1743-3533 (on-line)
doi:10.2495/DEB080041

local governments are often delayed due to the hesitation of the governmental officer or some human mistakes, and the delayed warnings have resulted severe damage. Consequently, disaster information should be conveyed directly to affected populations as soon as possible.

The current study develops a disaster information system that conveys information directly to residents in rural areas.

2 Prediction of debris flow using cumulative rainfall amount

Previous experimental results [1] have indicated that debris flow occurs when surface flow appears on a slope due to heavy rainfall. Solving the momentum and continuity equations for subsurface conditions using the kinematic wave theory, the occurrence conditions for surface flow are derived as

$$l \geq \frac{kT \sin \theta}{\lambda},$$ (1)

$$\lambda D = \int_0^T r \cos \theta dt,$$ (2)

where l is the length of the slope, k is the hydraulic conductivity, θ is the angle of slope, λ is the porosity, T is the time of concentration, D is the depth of the deposits, and r is the rainfall intensity.

Assuming that debris flow occurs when surface flow appears on a slope, the occurrence criteria for debris flow based on eqn. (1) and eqn. (2) are expressed as

$$\frac{1}{T} \int_0^T r dt \geq \frac{Dk}{l} \tan \theta$$

or (3)

$$R(t,T) = \int_{t-T}^T r(\tau)d\tau \geq \frac{Dk}{l} \tan \theta = R_c$$

where R is the cumulative rainfall amount and T is the time of concentration.

Equation (3) indicates that debris flow will occur when cumulative rainfall within the time of concentration exceeds a certain value related to the properties of the slope. Hirano et al. [2] proposed a system analysis technique to identify parameters to predict the occurrence of debris flow. To estimate the time of concentration T and critical rainfall Rc, Hirano et al. defined cumulative rainfall $R(t,\tau)$ as

$$R_{max}(\tau) = \max R(t,T),$$ (4)

$$R(t,T) = \int_{t-T}^T r(\tau)d\tau \geq \frac{Dk}{l} \tan \theta = R_c.$$ (5)

The maximum values of $R(t,\tau)$ for each time, $Rmax(\tau)$, are plotted against τ. If there are no errors in the data or in the theory, the plotted lines should exceed point $Rmax(T) = Rc$ when debris flow occurs, and should fall below the point when debris flow does not occur, shown schematically in Figure 1. Consequently, the upper limit line of non-occurrence and the lower limit line of occurrence should cross near point (T, Rc), as illustrated in Figure 2(a). Errors in the data as well as in the theory will prevent the intersection of these two curves, which will remain separated as shown in Figure 2(b). The time of concentration is estimated by the point where the difference between two curves is minimized.

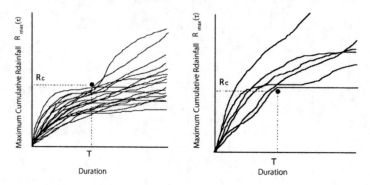

Figure 1:   Lower limit of occurrence and upper limit of non-occurrence.

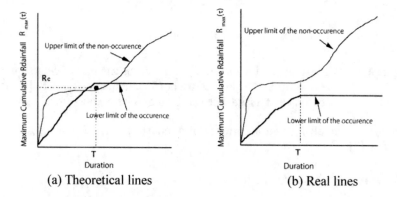

(a) Theoretical lines   (b) Real lines

Figure 2:   Critical lines, maximum cumulative rainfall and concentration time.

3   Application to actual debris flows

The data are available for debris flow occurrence in Kagoshima Prefecture in 1969, 1971, 1993 and 1997.

The maximum value $Rmax(\tau)$ for the cumulative time τ of each rainfall event is calculated using eqn.(4) and shown in Figure 3. The minimum cumulative rainfall amount for occurrence of debris flow was determined to be 121 mm for a 3-hour duration and the maximum cumulative rainfall amount of non-occurrence was also 121 mm for a 3-hour duration [3]. In the same way, the maximum

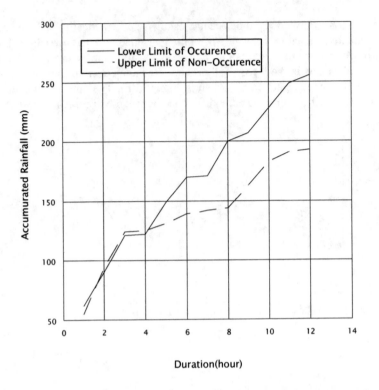

Figure 3: Critical maximum cumulative rainfall for analysis of debris flow in the Akune and Izumi Districts [3] cumulative rainfall for non-occurrence of a landslide was 88 mm for a-3 hour duration [3].

cumulative rainfall for non-occurrence of a landslide was 88 mm for a 3-hour duration [3].

4 Dynamic hazard map

Radar data observed by the Ministry of Land, Transportation and Infrastructure of Japan were utilized to develop the dynamic hazard map. The spatial resolution is approximately 1 square km and the temporal resolution is 5 minutes. The study area includes Kyushu and Shikoku Islands and the Chugoku area of Honshu Island, Japan.

Radar data for heavy rainfall observed from 19 to 23 July 2006 were used. These data are recorded using the XML database "eXist" [4] at the Sojo University laboratory. Using the estimated critical limit for cumulative rainfall defined above, a dynamic hazard map was derived based on the cumulative rainfall amount recorded by the precipitation radar. Figure 4 shows an example of a dynamic hazard map for the Minamata District area observed on 22 July 2006. A concentration time of 3 hours was used to generate the dynamic hazard map in real time. Events with greater than 88 mm of cumulative rainfall in

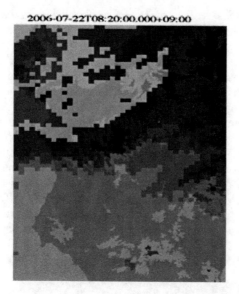

Figure 4:   Example of the dynamic hazard map.

3 hours may result in the occurrence of a landslide and rain in excess of 121 mm in 3 hours indicates the certain occurrence of debris flow. The former is indicated as yellow mesh and the latter is indicated as red mesh on the dynamic hazard map.

Java programming language was used to generate the dynamic hazard map. This program accesses the XML database "eXist" and retrieves rainfall data for three-hour intervals, which are used to calculate cumulative rainfall amounts. The cumulative rainfall values are converted to XML data format, allowing disaster information to be transmitted using the system described in the next chapter.

5   Dynamic hazard aerial map displayed on social network service

Disaster prevention information systems should maintain high levels of reliability for information. Internet Bulletin Board Systems (BBS) occasionally include inaccurate, malicious or incorrect information. Anonymous posts to bulletin boards are particularly unreliable. BBS should not serve as primary means for official communication. Moreover, most local governments are hesitant to issue evacuation orders despite the urgency of timely announcements because of the suddenness of debris flows.

Internet social network services (SNS) provide access to users, which must be registered by providing individual information. Consequently, SNS are able to identify the sender of information to some degree and can confirm the reliability of information provided to the network by registered enrollees, in contrast to internet BBS. SNS are able to minimize the delay of hazard information transmission by securing the source and reliability of the hazard information posts.

Drupal is a content management platform that allows an individual or community of users to easily publish, manage, and organize a wide variety of content on a website. [5]. Our disaster prevention information system was created using Drupal employing Invite, Buddylist and User Relationships modules to generate a SNS that coordinates registered user information with GIS data. The Flex2 version of Modestmaps is used to develop our GIS system. Modestmaps is a BSD-licensed display and interaction library for tile-based maps in Flash and Flex2 [6]. Flex2 and Drupal exchange the data through the Internet using the Action Message Format (AMF). AMF is a proprietary data format created by Macromedia (now Adobe) and used by different mediums. In the current study, the AMFPHP module of Drupal is used to connect Flash as client side and Drupal as server side for high–speed data exchange.

Figure 5:   Macro photograph of the barrier to prevent landslides constructed at the site of a debris flow in the Minamata District (highest resolution aerial photograph).

The GIS supported by Flash and Drupal is called "giSight", which displays the tile maps with free scroll, served by Yahoo! Maps or Virtual Earth with Modestmaps. The high-resolution aerial photographs for the Minamata District obtained from Kumamoto Prefecture can also be utilized as tile maps. These tile maps are served by Kumamoto Prefecture and stored on Amazon S3 [7], which is an inexpensive unlimited storage service. The highest resolution of the aerial photographs collected by Kumamoto Prefecture is 20 cm/pixel. Figure 5 shows a

Figure 6:   Example of giSight that displays markers for the Minamata District.

Figure 7:   Example of a dynamic hazard map for landslide and debris flow.

macro photograph of a dam constructed to prevent debris flow at the site of a debris flow in the Minamata District on 23 July 2003. Lines and polygons can be added to the map as markers using the Flash client. Figure 6 shows an example of giSight that displays the markers for the Minamata District.

Figure 7 shows an example the dynamic hazard map, which displays landslide and debris flow. Each 1-km mesh polygon contains the date and time, latitude and longitude and three-hour cumulative rainfall value and the data can be

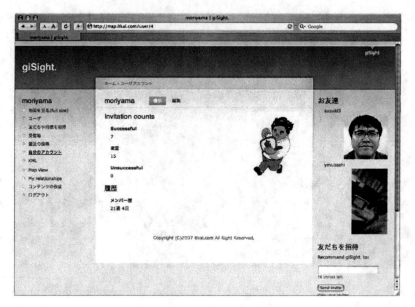

Figure 8:   SNS photo list of friends.

accessed by clicking on the polygon. Figure 8 shows an example of the SNS function, a photo list of friends (registered users).

6 Conclusion

The giSight displays landslide and debris flow in real-time on a hazard map and provides the GIS data to residents using the SNS. giSight is able to provide quick delivery of hazard information as conditions indicate the potential for a landslide or debris flow. This system is not only useful for disaster prevention, but also enables the distribution of aerial information to local residents.

References

[1] Hirano, M., Iwamoto, M. and Harada, T., Study on the mechanism of occurrence of debris flow by artificial rainfall, *Preprints of the annual meeting of JSCE*, Tokyo, pp. 299-301, 1976 (in Japanese).
[2] Hirano, M., Hikida, M. and Moriyama, T., Field observation and prediction of the hydrograph of volcanic debris flow, *Proceedings of the Fourth Congress of Asian and Pacific Regional Division of IAHR*, Bankok, Vol.1, pp. 287-298, 1984
[3] Moriyama, T. & Hikida, M., Rainfall Analysis of Debris Flow Occurrence in 2003, Minamata, Japan, *Proc. of 2nd APHW*, Singapore, 2004
[4] eXist, exist.sourceforge.net
[5] Drupal, drupal.org
[6] Modestmaps, modestmaps.com
[7] Amazon S3, www.amazon.com/gp/browse.html?node=16427261

A feasibility study on ECT monitoring of phase migration in porous solids

S. Liu[1], J. Liu[2] & Q. Chen[3]
[1]*School of Energy and Power Engineering,*
North China Electric Power University, Beijing 102206, China
[2]*Institute of Engineering Thermophysics, CAS, Beijing 100080, China*
[3]*School of Mechanics and Control Engineering,*
Beijing Jiaotong University, Beijing 100044, China

Abstract

In the study of the strength of soil/sand, and the cause of the incipience of debris flow, it is important to monitor the distribution and the migration of ice and water contents in such porous media. To overcome the difficulty of "seeing" through opaque soil, an experimental investigation was conducted to explore the feasibility of non-intrusive monitoring of ice migration in porous media by using electric capacitance tomography (ECT). A ten-electrode sensor was made for signal acquisition and OIOR method was used for image reconstruction. The distribution and penetration of ice in porous solids are displayed clearly by ECT images. ECT data were also validated against the temperature data measured by thermocouples, and the feasibility of such ECT method is convincingly proven.
Keywords: flow monitoring, flow in porous solids.

1 Introduction

Ice penetration or melting in soil/sand (porous solids) can significantly alter the stability of the solid matrix, which will affect the possibility of debris/rock flow. Therefore, it is important to understand the relationship between ice penetration or melting in soil and the corresponding change in the mechanical properties of the soil. However, it is difficult to monitor ice and water contents and their migration in such porous media by conventional techniques, due to the limited sensing accessibility, e.g. opacity, of the solids.

Electrical Capacitance Tomography (ECT) is a recently developed non-intrusive technique for visualizing the distribution of materials. As an example,

WIT Transactions on Engineering Sciences, Vol 60, © 2008 WIT Press
www.witpress.com, ISSN 1743-3533 (on-line)
doi:10.2495/DEB080051

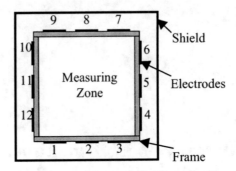

Figure 1:   ECT sensor.

figure 1 is a sketch of a twelve-electrode ECT sensor. The electrodes are numbered from 1 to 12. Inside the frame is the measuring zone. Surrounding the electrodes is a metal shield. ECT does not disturb the process inside the measuring zone, and images are produced via image reconstruction algorithms [1]. It is the purpose of this study to examine the feasibility of ECT to visualize the distribution and migration of ice and water contents in porous solids, aiming at further development of ECT into a viable monitoring technique for the study of ice penetration or melting in soil.

For a sensor of x electrodes, the number of independent capacitance measurements is $m = C_x^2 = x(x-1)/2$ and the measured capacitances are represented by an array $\mathbf{C} = (C_1, C_2, \ldots, C_m)^T$. An ECT image is reconstructed based on the values of the capacitances. Usually a measuring zone is virtually divided into, say n, pixels, then the distribution of the objects in the measuring zone is represented by an array of grey values on the pixels, i.e. $\mathbf{G} = (G_1, G_2, \ldots, G_n)^T$, where G_i is the grey value on pixel i.

One of the most earlier and common image reconstruction method is Linear Back Projection, LBP, in which a linear relationship between C and G is assumed:

$$\mathbf{C} = \mathbf{SG} \qquad (1)$$

where $\mathbf{S} \in R^{m \times n}$ is a coefficient matrix, commonly called sensitivity map. The descriptions of the methods to derive $\mathbf{S}$ are abundant in the literature, e.g. Xie et al. [2].

LBP reconstructs images according to:

$$\mathbf{G} = \mathbf{S}^T \mathbf{C} \qquad (2)$$

where $\mathbf{S}^T$ is the transpose of $\mathbf{S}$.

LBP is simple and fast, but often suffers from the problems of notorious "ill-posed" nature, i.e. the severe deficit of the measured data with regard to the large number of pixels. The quality of LBP is often poor.

To improve the quality of the images, various image reconstruction techniques have been developed over the years [3–6]. Among them iterative methods have been widely applied.

A most widely applied iterative method is the Landweber [3] method that repeatedly applies equation (1) (forward process) and equation (2) (inverse process) to gradually reduce the errors, as described by:

$$\mathbf{G}_0 = \mathbf{S}^T\mathbf{C} \tag{3}$$

$$\mathbf{G}_{k+1} = \mathbf{G}_k + \alpha_k \mathbf{S}^T(\mathbf{C} - \mathbf{S}\mathbf{G}_k) = \mathbf{G}_k + \alpha_k \mathbf{S}^T\mathbf{e}_k, \quad (k = 0, 1, 2, \cdots) \tag{4}$$

$$\mathbf{G}_{final} = \mathbf{G}_{final-1}, \quad \text{when } \mathbf{e}^{(k)} < \text{certain criterion} \tag{5}$$

Due to the correction in each step, the new images are expected to gradually approach the true image. The process continues until a certain criterion is met, e.g. $\|(\mathbf{C} - \mathbf{S}\mathbf{G}_k)\| / \|\mathbf{C}\| < 0.01$.

However, an inherit drawback of the iterative methods is the cost of time. It has long been desired for an ECT system to perform "online iteration", i.e. to take measurements with the quality of an iterative method whilst maintaining the advantage of fast speed. For this, a new method, namely OIOR (Offline-Iteration-Online-Reconstruction), has been developed by the authors [7].

OIOR has two parts, in the first part the iterations are performed offline to obtain a matrix $\mathbf{D}_z$ of the same dimensions as the transpose of the sensitivity map: i.e.

$$\mathbf{D}_0 = \mathbf{S}^T \tag{6}$$

$$\mathbf{D}_{k+1} = \mathbf{A}_k\mathbf{D}_k + \mathbf{B}_k = (\mathbf{I} - \alpha_k\mathbf{S}^T\mathbf{S})\mathbf{D}_k + \alpha_k\mathbf{S}^T$$
$$= \mathbf{D}_k + \alpha_k\mathbf{S}^T(\mathbf{I} - \mathbf{S}\mathbf{D}_k) \quad (k = 1, 2, \cdots, z) \tag{7}$$

in which $\mathbf{I} \in \mathbf{R}^{m \times m}$ is an identity matrix.

In the second stage an images is reconstructed in the same way as LBP, but using matrix $\mathbf{D}_z$:

$$\mathbf{G} = \mathbf{D}_z\mathbf{C} \tag{8}$$

Equation (8) is of exactly the same form as LBP, meaning that the algorithm will have the same image reconstruction speed as LBP, i.e. it can be used for online measurement like LBP does. However, as $\mathbf{D}_z$ is the result after many iterations, equation (8) will yield improved image quality as an iterative method does. Therefore, the new algorithm is effectively an online iterative image reconstruction method.

2 Experimental

2.1 Test apparatus

To study ice propagation in porous solids, a test unit is built shown in figure 2. The centre zone, depicted by A-B-D-C, is the test zone wherein the ice propagation occurs. Temperatures on the upper cover and the lower cover are controlled individually by circulating a liquid coolant, so that a temperature gradient can be maintained at desired values.

As the top and the bottom surfaces are unavailable for ECT electrodes, the ECT sensor has to be in an unclosed structure with electrodes arranged only on the two sides, depicted in figure 2. The ECT sensor has ten electrodes, five on each side, with a radial guard placed between each pair of electrodes. An insulating wrap covers the sensor. This unique feature requires a specially designed sensitivity map for image reconstruction.

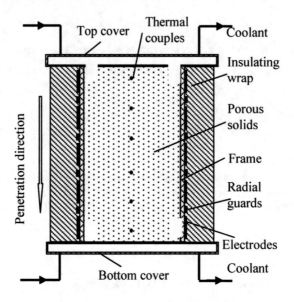

Figure 2:   Sketch of the test unit.

There are also six thermocouples placed in the test medium, all along the central line, to provide some referencing indications of the temperature distributions inside.

The ECT device is an AC based system, comprised of the sensor, the data acquisition electronics, and a computer for data processing, as depicted in figure 3. The excitation voltage is a 15 V sine wave with a frequency of 200 KHz. Data collection speed is can be adjusted up to 140 frames per second. More details about the device can be found in [1].

2.2 Experimental procedures

The test medium, namely sand, was first dried thoroughly in an oven. Then a proper amount of water was fully mixed with the solids to achieve desired moisture content. In this study, 5% water content was selected for all the experiments. The test medium was then sealed in a glass jar for 24 hours to reach uniform distribution of the moisture in the solids. After that, the test medium was filled into the test section and temperatures at the top and bottom covers were adjusted to the desired temperature gradient. Ice then began to form and ice front started to move from the top cover to the bottom cover.

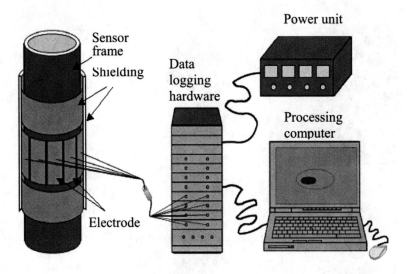

Figure 3:   ECT system.

ECT measurements were then taken to image the ice distribution and motion inside the measuring zone. OIOR method, i.e. equation (8), was used for image reconstruction. As ice movement was slow, a 10 frame/second data acquisition speed would be sufficient.

3 Results and discussions

Figures 4–9 (a)s and (b)s show respectively the 2D and 3D images acquired by ECT, while (c)s show the temperatures profile along the centre line. Because the experiment begins with purely wet sand in the test zone, therefore, the permittivity is the highest in figure 4 (a) and (b), and the grey levels of the pixels of the image are generally high. When frozen zone forms, the permittivity decreases and the grey levels of the image pixels reduce in zone I, see figure 5 (a) and (b). As the frozen zone extends deeper, the low permittivity zone follows as well, reflected by the lighter color in (a)s and lower surfaces in (b)s of the figures. This continues until ice zone occupies almost all the test zone, shown in figure 9. In figures 5–8 (a)-(b) it can be seen that after a certain length of time, i.e. 3.3, 3.8, 5.5 and 5.9 hour respectively, the tip of the ice front correspondingly reaches positions roughly 58mm (red dotted line), 50, 35 and 20mm above the bottom.

The temperature profiles measured by the thermocouples are used to compare with the ECT results. Figures 4–9 (c)s show temperature distribution alone the freezing direction, i.e. the axial line of the test zone. Before freezing takes place, the temperature is about 20.4°C at all the points, and the temperatures drop after freeing. In fact, the freezing point corresponding to 5% water content is -0.42 °C, as indicated by the dotted lines in the figures. Therefore, judging from the

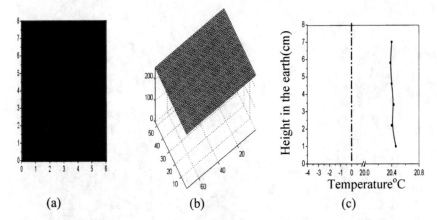

(a)   (b)   (c)

Figure 4:   ECT images and temperature before freezing (t=0h)

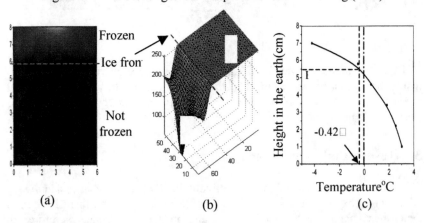

(a)   (b)   (c)

Figure 5:   ECT images and temperature profile when t=3.3h.

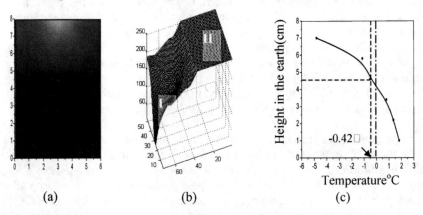

(a)   (b)   (c)

Figure 6:   ECT images and temperature profile when t=3.8h.

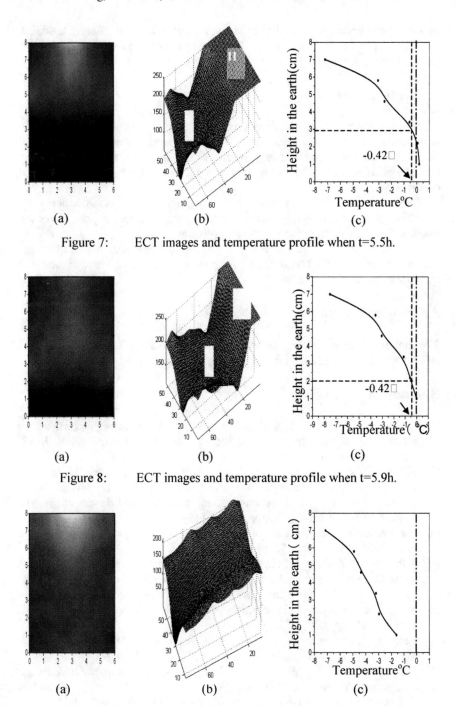

Figure 7:   ECT images and temperature profile when t=5.5h.

Figure 8:   ECT images and temperature profile when t=5.9h.

Figure 9:   ECT images and temperature profile when t=7.8h.

figures, it can been seen that the ice front researches approximately 54, 46, 29, and 20mm above the bottom cover, when time span is 3.3, 3.8, 5.5, and 5.9 hours respectively.

4 Conclusions

ECT measurements of ice distribution and motion in porous materials have been successful in the current investigation. The non-intrusive measuring method of ECT can be advantageous for materials of opaque nature, and enables monitoring of material distributions inside the measuring zone without disturbing the real condition.

ECT data are also compared with the temperature measurements by thermocouples and reasonably good agreements are obtained, which proves the feasibility of ECT method for the current problems.

As such a method is new and still in its developing stage, more studies are needed to gain detailed understanding both of ECT measurement and the mechanism of ice motion in soil.

Acknowledgements

The authors wish to express their gratitude to CAS (KZCX2-YW-302) and NSFC (60672151, 60532020) for sponsoring this study.

References

[1] Liu, S., Wang, H. G., Jiang, F. & Yang, W. Q., A new image reconstruction method for tomographic investigation of fluidized beds, *AIChE J*, **48**, pp. 1631–1638, 2002.
[2] Xie, C., Huang, S., Hoyle, B. S., Thorn, R., Lenn, C., Snowden, D. & Beck, M. S., Electrical capacitance tomography for flow imaging: system model for development of image reconstruction algorithms and design of primary sensors, in *IEE Proc.-G*, **139**, pp. 89–97,. 1992.
[3] Landweber, L., An iterative formula for Fredholm integral equations of the first kind, *Amer. J. Math*,**73**, pp. 615–624, 1951.
[4] Yang, W. Q. & Peng, L. H., Image reconstruction algorithms for electrical capacitance tomography, *Meas. Sci. Technol.*, **14**, pp. R1–R13, 2003.
[5] Liu, S., Fu, L. & Yang, W. Q., Optimization of iterative image reconstruction process for electrical capacitance tomography, *Meas. Sci. Technol.*, **10**, pp. L37–L39, 1999.
[6] Isaksen, ∅. & Nordtvedt, J. E., A new reconstruction algorithm for process tomography, *Meas. Sci. and Technol.*, **4**, pp. 1464–1475, 1993.
[7] Liu, S., Fu, L., Yang, W. Q., Wang, H. & Jiang, F., On-line Iterative Image Reconstruction for ECT, *Proceedings of the 3rd World Congress on Industrial Process Tomography*, Banff, Canada, pp. 403–408, 2003.

Development of "Kanako", a wide use 1-D and 2-D debris flow simulator equipped with GUI

K. Nakatani, T. Wada, Y. Satofuka & T. Mizuyama
Laboratory of Erosion Control, Graduate School of Agriculture, Kyoto University, Japan

Abstract

Debris flows often cause substantial losses to human life and the economy. Damage can be effectively reduced using numerical simulation models, which can describe the debris flow process and determine possible effects of sabo dams, or erosion and sediment control dams. However, non-experts find it very difficult to run simulations independently, because the systems do not currently have an efficient user interface. We developed a system that produces one- and two-dimensional debris flow simulations and is equipped with a graphical user interface (GUI). The system is based on an integration model and employs one-dimensional simulations for gully areas and two-dimensional simulations for alluvial fan areas, and then considers their mutual influence in boundary areas between gullies and alluvial fans. The system was developed with "MS Visual Basic.NET." Data can be input using a mouse and be checked on the monitor, users can see real-time visualized images of the debris flow during the simulation. The interface enables non-expert users to run the debris-flow simulation independently, enabling better solutions for sabo engineering.

Keywords: debris flow, graphical user interface (GUI), numerical simulation, one- and two-dimensional integration model.

1 Introduction

Debris flows can cause severe damage in gullies and alluvial fans and Sabo works is to reduce and prevent sediment disaster such as debris flows. Sabo dams, or erosion and sediment control dams, effectively prevent and reduce disasters caused by debris flow, and many sabo dams have been constructed in Japan. These dams can reduce the energy of a debris flow, thereby controlling

WIT Transactions on Engineering Sciences, Vol 60, © 2008 WIT Press
www.witpress.com, ISSN 1743-3533 (on-line)
doi:10.2495/DEB080061

the surface erosion that usually occurs in upstream areas. For most efficient results, sabo dam design (e.g. type, location, size) must be customized to each specific area. Researchers have recently proposed a variety of numerical simulation models (Takahama *et al.* [1], Egashira and Itoh [2]) and some have been put to practical use when designing sabo dams.

However, many users have not been enthusiastic about these systems. The processes and display are difficult to understand and require specific training to operate, and users find it difficult to prepare the various datasets and parameters. Thus, users who are not experts on debris flow simulation (e.g. sabo engineers) are unable to run simulations independently and are forced to rely on specialists.

As models become increasingly complex, the knowledge gap between specialists and engineers is widening, making simulations a complicated and impractical tool for sabo engineering. If researchers continue to focus on debris flow simulations by simply testing the accuracy of existing models or developing new models, the systems will continue to be impractical.

To address this problem, we developed a system equipped with a user-friendly graphical user interface (GUI), which will enable non-experts to run numerical debris flow simulations independently.

2 Kanako Ver.2.00 system

2.1 Platform

We developed our system using MS Visual Basic.NET (VB) because this platform was designed to run on Windows. It also provides an interactive GUI and is easy for beginners to learn. There is a common misunderstanding that VB performance is easy to use but has low-function, but VB is actually both easy to use and yields high performance. Because the platform is so widely used and easy to learn, users can easily modify and extend the system.

2.2 Graphical user interface (GUI)

A user interface is the means by which users interact with a particular machine, device, computer program, or the system. A GUI enables users to interact with media formats (e.g. PC) that employ graphical icons to represent information and available actions to a user. Users normally perform actions by directly manipulating the graphical elements.

To ensure the system easy for beginners to use, datasets used in simulations can be input using a mouse and checked on the monitor. Users can view real-time images of debris flows, hydrographs, and the effects of sabo dams, during the simulation. The GUI enables users without specialized training to identify better solutions effectively and to run debris-flow simulations independently.

2.3 Developed system

Our GUI-equipped debris flow simulator is called "Kanako." Kanako Ver.1.10 (Nakatani *et al.* [3]) can simulate one-dimensional (1-D) debris flow and the effects of sabo dams. In this study, we developed Kanako Ver.2.00, which can simulate 1-D debris flow in gullies and two-dimensional (2-D) debris flow in alluvial fans.

3   Numerical simulation model

The system applies an integration model (Wada *et al.* [4]). For gullies, it uses a 1-D numerical simulation model to reproduce variations in a mountain riverbed caused by debris flow and to simulate the effects of closed, slit, and grid types of sabo dams (Satofuka and Izuyama [5]). For alluvial fans, it uses a 2-D numerical simulation model to reproduce changes in flow depth and sedimentation to simulate the passing area of debris flow.

Previous models have simulated the boundary areas between gullies and alluvial fans using the 1-D downstream end result as the 2-D upstream boundary condition. In contrast, our integration model simulates both 1-D results for gullies and 2-D results for alluvial fans at each time step, incorporating mutual influences of both models. This enables the system to reproduce more accurate results, especially when marked sedimentation occurs in a boundary area.

3.1   Governing equations for debris flow

The basic 2-D debris flow equations are shown below. The same equations are applied in 1-D debris flow simulations without *y*-axis direction terms. Momentum equations, continuation equations, riverbed deformation equations, erosion/deposition equations, and riverbed shearing stress are based on Takahashi and Kuang [6], and the staggered scheme and arrangement of variables are based on Takahashi and Nakagawa [7].

The continuation equation for the total volume of debris flow is:

$$\frac{\partial h}{\partial t} + \frac{\partial uh}{\partial x} + \frac{\partial vh}{\partial y} = i \tag{1}$$

The continuation equation for determining particle *k*th grade is:

$$\frac{\partial C_k h}{\partial t} + \frac{\partial C_k hu}{\partial x} + \frac{\partial C_k hv}{\partial y} = i_k C_* \tag{2}$$

Here, we can consider two grain-size classes for sediment material.
The phenomenon of *x*-axis direction (flow-direction) flow uses a momentum equation, as follows:

$$\frac{\partial u}{\partial t} + u\frac{\partial u}{\partial x} + v\frac{\partial u}{\partial y} = g\sin\theta_{wx} - \frac{\tau_x}{\rho h} \tag{3}$$

The phenomenon of *y*-axis direction (cross-direction) flow uses a momentum equation, as follows:

$$\frac{\partial v}{\partial t} + u\frac{\partial v}{\partial x} + v\frac{\partial v}{\partial y} = g\sin\theta_{wy} - \frac{\tau_y}{\rho h} \tag{4}$$

The equation for determining change in bed surface elevation is as follows:

$$\frac{\partial z}{\partial t} + i = 0 \tag{5}$$

For eqn (1) through (5), h is flow depth, u is x-axis direction flow velocity, v is y-axis direction flow velocity, C_k is kth sediment concentration by volume in debris flow, z is bed elevation, t is time, i is erosion/deposition velocity, i_k is kth sediment erosion/deposition velocity, g is gravity acceleration, ρ is interstitial fluid density, θ_{wx} and θ_{wy} are the flow surface gradients in the x-axis and y-axis directions, C_* is sediment concentration by volume in movable bed layer, and τ_x and τ_y are the riverbed shearing stresses in the x-axis and y-axis directions.

3.2 Conditions for sabo dam design and simulation variables

The numerical simulation model applies a staggered scheme using a finite difference method. Scalar and vector quantities are staggered by $\Delta x/2$ (or $\Delta y/2$) in the flow direction (or cross direction), as shown in Fig. 1. Sabo dams are set at the calculation point of flow velocity, as shown in Fig. 2. The effective flow depth, h', at the dam point, which is used to calculate the outflow flux, is expressed using the variables shown in Fig. 2, as follows:

$$h' = \begin{cases} h_i + z_i - z_d & (h_i + z_i - z_d \geq 0) \\ 0 & (h_i + z_i - z_d < 0) \\ h_i & (z_i > z_d) \end{cases} \tag{6}$$

where z_d is the dam crest elevation, which is the sum of bed elevation and dam height. Here, h_i is flow depth in the scalar evaluation point next to the dam position in the upstream direction and z_i is the riverbed height at the same point as h_i (fig. 2). In addition, at vector evaluation points where the sabo dam is not set, flow discharge is calculated using upstream side flow depth and velocity.

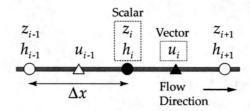

Figure 1:   Arrangement of variables in a 1-D area.

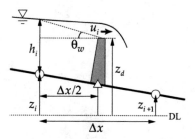

Figure 2:   Arrangement of variables at a sabo dam.

3.2.1 Simulation of a closed type sabo dam

To examine upstream deposition velocity in a closed sabo dam, we can use a previously developed method (Takahashi *et al.* [8]) to calculate variations in a riverbed. This method uses a relationship between dam height and riverbed height at the dam's upper site to determine whether materials will pass over a sabo dam. When a dam's upstream side contains a pocket, materials and water can be separated easily. When the riverbed height is lower than dam height ($z_i < z_d$), materials supplied from upstream are immediately deposited at that point.

3.2.2 Simulation of a slit type sabo dam

Kanako can simulate the effect of a slit sabo dam. When a slit dam is set, the system simulates the narrowing river width between upstream and downstream scalar evaluation points, from the vector evaluation point where the sabo dam is set. However, the model does not currently incorporate energy loss from the sharp narrowing of river width.

3.2.3 Simulation of a grid type sabo dam

When debris flows occurs in a mountainous river where a grid sabo dam is set, the opening of the grid dam is blocked by large rocks in the front part of the debris flow, which can cause the dam to trap the subsequent muddy flow as a closed type dam. In the model developed by Satofuka and Mizuyama [9], a grid dam is treated as a closed dam with a temporally variable height through the blockage. In the model, sediment material is composed of two grain-size classes; only the larger class of sediment causes stoppage of the grid dam opening and increases the dam height. The model estimates temporal changes in dam height using probabilities of the blockage being influenced by sediment concentration, flow depth, sediment diameter, and distance of grid dam columns.

3.3 Integration model

3.3.1 Outline of the integration model

Fig. 3 presents the integration model outline. It enables continual simulation of both 1-D models in gullies and 2-D models in alluvial fans at each time step.

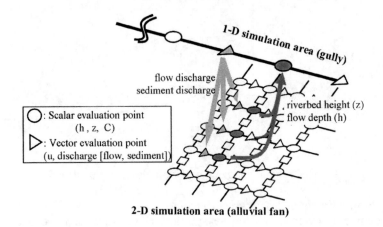

Figure 3:   Outline of the integration model.

Using the 1-D downstream end-flow discharge and sediment discharge as the 2-D upstream inflow condition and using 2-D simulated riverbed height and flow depth as the 1-D downstream end condition, the integration model incorporates mutual influences of the 1-D and 2-D simulations. Moreover, this integration model can handle situations in which intervals of 2-D cross direction calculation points and 1-D river width differ or 1-D simulation flow direction and 2-D simulation flow (x-axis) direction differ slightly.

3.3.2 Integration of 1-D and 2-D simulation areas

The 1-D downstream end calculation point number is set as ie, and the inflow point in the 2-D upstream end area's grid point coordinates are set as $(1, jc)$. Fig. 4 shows the integration of 1-D and 2-D areas, corresponding to the 1-D No. $(ie - 1)$ vector evaluation point with the 2-D $(1, jc)$ vector evaluation point. In Fig. 4, Δx_1 shows the calculation point interval in 1-D, Δx_2 shows the x-axis direction

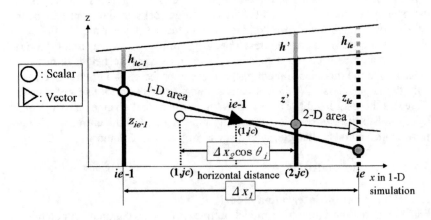

Figure 4:   Profile of the integration area.

grid interval in 2-D, h_i and z_i reproduce the flow depth and riverbed elevation of the 1-D area No. i point, h' and z' reproduce the average flow depth and riverbed elevation of the 2-D area upstream end, and θ_i shows the angle between the 1-D x-axis and the 2-D x-axis. To integrate different dimensional simulation areas, we have to consider θ_i.

As shown in Fig. 5, the 2-D grid interval in the x-axis direction is transformed to $\Delta x_2 \cos \theta_i$ in the 1-D area, and the 1-D No. (ie-1) vector evaluation point river width is shown as $B_{ie-1} / \cos \theta_i$ in the 2-D area. In Fig. 5, B_{ie-1} shows the river width at the 1-D No. (ie-1) vector evaluation point, and Δy_2 shows the 2-D grid interval in the y-axis direction.

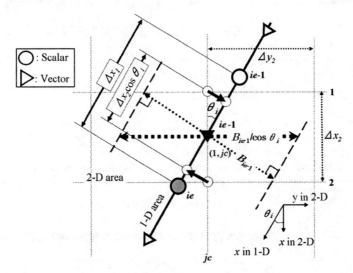

Figure 5:   Plan of the integration area.

4   Outline of Kanako Ver.2.00

4.1 Setting input data

In the Kanako start screen (fig. 6), the graphic displayed in the upper part is the 1-D riverbed profile, and the river width is in the middle, presented in meters.

The riverbed profile includes three parameters; the surface of the moveable bed, the surface of the fixed bed, and the river width. Each can be modified by dragging the point. Yellow points on the riverbed profile indicate hydrograph observation points, and black, gray, and blue checked rectangles indicate closed, slit, and grid type sabo dams. When a point is dragged, a guide appears to reveal the current position. Sabo dam parameters can be set in the sabo dam detail screen. User can set these by double-clicking on the sabo dam, causing a pop-up window of detailed dam settings to appear. Variable settings include height, type (closed, slit, or grid), and slit width can be set using text boxes or radio buttons. Other details for a grid type of sabo dam, such as column diameter and distance between columns, can be set in another screen. Dam position can be adjusted by dragging the rectangle right or left along the river profile. Supplied hydrograph from the upstream end and the number of calculation points can be set in other pop-up windows.

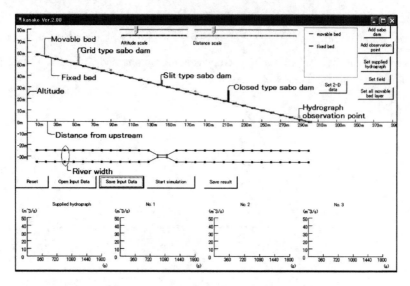

Figure 6:   Kanako Ver.2.00 start screen.

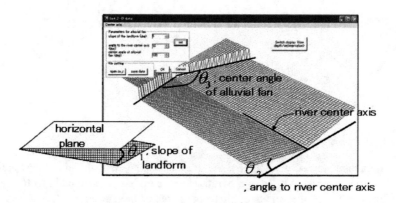

Figure 7:   2-D landform setting.

To set 2-D landform conditions, open 'set 2-D landform' window (fig. 7) and set parameters in group box; slope of the landform, angle to the river center axis, and center angle of the alluvial fan, shown as θ_1, θ_2, and θ_3 in fig. 7.

4.2 Running a simulation

As the simulation starts by clicking 'Start' button, debris flow is initiated and moves down from the upper stream. The 1-D simulation screen animates real-time image of flow depth, moving bed surface, initial bed surface, and fixed bed in the upper screen (fig. 8). Four graphs displayed at the bottom represent hydrograph and sediment graph, supplied from the upstream end and at each observation point. Here, the vertical axis represents debris flow discharge (m^3/s) and the horizontal axis represents time (s). After debris flow reaches the alluvial fan, the 2-D simulation screen animates (fig. 9) flow depth and sedimentation to represent the passing area of debris flow.

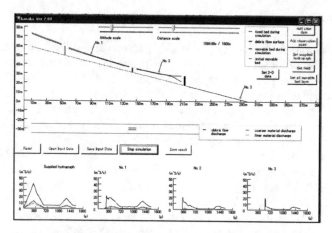

Figure 8:   1-D simulation screen.

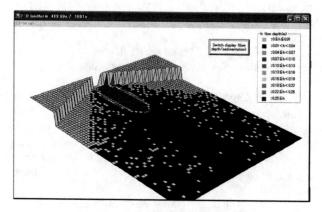

Figure 9:   2-D simulation screen showing flow depth.

The simulator calculates for a period of 1800 s and stops. User can preserve simulation results as a CSV data file following normal procedures for saving data.

5 Conclusions

Kanako 2.00 is easier to use and provides more information to users than previously developed simulators. Users can easily input calculation conditions based on their needs, by using a mouse to click on the menu functions, and can check data using the displayed graphics. Simulation results can be understood intuitively. Therefore, users can conduct numerical simulations to calculate debris flow processes even without advanced training. In future research, we plan to improve the 2-D model with the use of GIS, so that Kanako can simulate debris flow from a mountainous river to alluvial fans from occurrence to stop.

References

[1] Takahama, J., Fujita, Y., Kondo, Y., Hachiya, K., Two-layer model for analysis of deposition and erosion processes of debris flows, *Annual Journal of Hydraulic Engineering, JSCE*, 46, pp. 677–682, 2002 (in Japanese with English summary).

[2] Egashira, S., Itoh, T., Numerical simulation of debris flow, *Journal of Japan Society of Computational Fluid Dynamics*, 12(2), Online (in Japanese) www.nagare.or.jp/jscfd/j-jscfd/122/p122-2.pdf.

[3] Nakatani, K., Satofuka, Y., Mizuyama, T., Development of 'KANAKO', a wide use debris flow simulator equipped with GUI, *Proc. of 32nd Congress of IAHR*, Venice, Italy, CD-ROM, 10p, A2.c-182, 2007.

[4] Wada, T., Satofuka, Y., Mizuyama T., Integration of 1- and 2-dimensional models for debris flow simulation, *Journal of the Japan Society of Erosion Control Engineering*, under review (in Japanese with English summary).

[5] Satofuka, Y., Mizuyama T., Numerical simulation of a debris flow in a mountainous river with a sabo dam, *Journal of the Japan Society of Erosion Control Engineering*, 58(1), pp. 14–19, 2005 (in Japanese with English summary).

[6] Takahashi, T., Kuang, S., Formation of debris flow on varied slope bed, *Disaster Prevention Research Institute Annuals*, 29(B-2), pp. 345–349, 1986.

[7] Takahashi, T., Nakagawa, H., Prediction of stony debris flow induced by severe rainfall, *Journal of the Japan Society of Erosion Control Engineering*, 44(3), pp. 12–19, 1991 (in Japanese with English summary).

[8] Takahashi, T., Nakagawa, H., Satofuka, Y., Kawaike, K., Flood and sediment disasters triggered by 1999 rainfall in Venezuela: A river restoration plan for an alluvial fan, *Journal of Natural Disaster Science*, 23, pp. 65–82, 2001.

[9] Satofuka, Y., Mizuyama, T., Numerical simulation of debris flow control by a grid dam, *Proc. of the 6th Japan-Taiwan Joint Seminar on Natural Hazard Mitigation*, CD-ROM, 2006.

Section 2
Debris flow modelling

Verification of a 2D finite element debris flow model using Bingham and cross rheological formulations

C. Martinez[1], F. Miralles-Wilhelm[1] & R. Garcia-Martinez[2]
[1]*Department of Civil and Environmental Engineering,
Florida International University, Miami, USA*
[2]*Applied Research Center, Florida International University,
Miami, USA*

Abstract

We propose a vertically-averaged 2D debris flow model based on the non-Newtonian Bingham and Cross rheological formulations. In the Cross model, fluid viscosity changes continuously through the range of shear rates. The 2D model is based on the shallow water equations, where the internal friction losses are implemented using the Cross constitutive relations. The numerical method is based on a four-step, selective lumping, explicit time stepping scheme. We present preliminary tests for one dimensional and two dimensional dam break problems. Model results show very good agreement with experimental data and analytical solutions in one dimensional cases. For the flow early stages, the numerical solution agrees better with the experimental data than with the analytical solution. However, in final stages, the numerical solution predicts that the fluid front advances more rapidly than the analytical solution and measured fluid front. The proposed 2D debris flow model provides very stable results even in the range of very low shear rates, where other discontinuous constitutive relations that use the yield stress may become unstable.
Keywords: debris flow, Cross model, Bingham model, yield stress, finite elements.

WIT Transactions on Engineering Sciences, Vol 60, © 2008 WIT Press
www.witpress.com, ISSN 1743-3533 (on-line)
doi:10.2495/DEB080071

1 Introduction

Mud and debris flows can be characterized as a flowing sediment-water mixture driven by gravity. Rheological studies of mud at high enough solid concentrations have shown that it behaves as a very viscous, non-Newtonian fluid, exhibiting a yield stress as evidenced by an minimum depth needed for a uniform layer of mud to flow. Various rheological models have been proposed [2, 3, 5, 10], being the Bingham plastic model the most commonly used in practice. In simple shear, the stress and shear rate relation for a Bingham fluid is:

$$\tau = \begin{cases} 0 & \text{if} \quad \tau < \tau_y \\ \tau_y + \mu\dot{\gamma} & \text{if} \quad \tau \geq \tau_y \end{cases} \tag{1}$$

where τ is the shear stress, τ_y is the yield stress, μ is the dynamic viscosity and $\dot{\gamma}$ is the shear rate. Many authors have proposed the Bingham rheological model to simulate debris flow. However, the hypothesis of a critical or yield shear stress may create instabilities in some model applications since, for close to zero shear rates, the Bingham model has a viscosity discontinuity where it changes from a finite value to infinity. This constitutes a phase change where the initially liquid fluid becomes a solid, rendering the fluid governing equations invalid. Although computationally this is not an insurmountable obstacle, it forces modelers to introduce not always well founded *ad hoc* assumptions for this low shear rate region. In this paper, we propose a 2D debris flow model based on the shallow water and sediment transport equations and the non-Newtonian Cross rheological formulation. The main peculiarity of the Cross formulation is that it considers that the fluid viscosity changes continuously from a finite value at high shear rates to a very high one (but much less than infinity) as the shear rate tends to zero. Theoretically, the model does not consider a yield stress and therefore the liquid fluid phase is always retained.

In this paper, we expand on the present preliminary results presented by Martinez *et al.* [9] of the proposed model that aim to test the stability and performance of the model at low shear rates by comparing against experimental data and the analytical solution given by Huang and Garcia [6, 7].

2 Governing equations

The model is based on the 2D shallow water equations that describe the free surface flow with the vertically averaged approximation and the sediment continuity equation in Cartesian coordinates:

$$\frac{\partial H}{\partial t} + \frac{\partial(\bar{u}H)}{\partial x} + \frac{\partial(\bar{v}H)}{\partial y} = 0 \tag{2}$$

$$\frac{\partial(\bar{c}H)}{\partial t} + \frac{\partial(\bar{c}\bar{u}H)}{\partial x} + \frac{\partial(\bar{c}\bar{v}H)}{\partial y} = 0 \tag{3}$$

$$\frac{\partial \bar{u}}{\partial t} + \bar{u}\frac{\partial \bar{u}}{\partial x} + \bar{v}\frac{\partial \bar{u}}{\partial y} + g\frac{\partial \eta}{\partial x} + S_{fx} = 0 \qquad (4)$$

$$\frac{\partial \bar{v}}{\partial t} + \bar{u}\frac{\partial \bar{v}}{\partial x} + \bar{v}\frac{\partial \bar{v}}{\partial y} + g\frac{\partial \eta}{\partial y} + S_{fy} = 0 \qquad (5)$$

where x and y are the horizontal coordinates, t is the time, η is the water surface elevation, H is the water depth, $\bar{c}$ is the vertically averaged sediment concentration, $\bar{u}$ and $\bar{v}$ are the vertically averaged velocities in directions x and y respectively, g is the gravitational acceleration and S_{fx} and S_{fy} are the depth integrated stress terms that depend on the rheological model to be used.

2.1 Implementation of rheological models

Using the quadratic model postulated by O'Brien and Julien [10]

$$\tau_{xz} = \tau_{y} + \mu\dot{\gamma} + \zeta\dot{\gamma}^{2} \qquad (6)$$

The first two terms are referred to as the Bingham shear stresses and represent the internal resistance stresses of a Bingham fluid. The last term represents the sum of the dispersive and turbulent shear stresses, which depend on the square of the shear rate.

When the shear stress relationship is depth integrated, it can be rewritten in the following slope form:

$$S_{fx} = S_{y} + S_{v} + S_{td} \qquad (7)$$

Where S_y is the yield slope, S_v is the viscous slope and S_{td} is the turbulent dispersive slope (O'Brien and Julien [10]). The yield slope is defined as:

$$S_{y} = \frac{\tau_{y}}{\rho g H} \qquad (8)$$

Assuming a vertical parabolic distribution for velocity u, the viscous slope is:

$$S_{v} = \frac{\mu\dot{\gamma}}{\rho g H} = \frac{3\mu\bar{u}}{\rho g H^{2}} \qquad (9)$$

For the quadratic term, O'Brien and Julien [10] suggest the use of Manning equation, yielding:

$$S_{td} = \frac{N^{2}\bar{u}^{2}}{H^{4/3}} \qquad (10)$$

The Manning coefficient of roughness N, is an empirically derived coefficient, which is dependent on many factors, including bottom surface roughness and sinuosity.

Finally, for the quadratic rheological model of O'Brien and Julien, the depth integrated stress term is

$$S_{fx} = \frac{\tau_y}{\rho g H} + \frac{3\mu \bar{u}}{\rho g H^2} + \frac{N^2 \bar{u}^2}{H^{4/3}} \tag{11}$$

The quadratic model of O'Brian and Julien is combined with the Cross formulation,

$$\tau_{xz} = \mu_{eff} \dot{\gamma} + \zeta \dot{\gamma}^2 \tag{12}$$

where μ_{eff} is the effective viscosity, a continuous variable that changes from a large value at very low shear rates to the fluid dynamic viscosity at higher shear rates. The effective viscosity can be conveniently defined in terms of the Bingham fluid parameters (yield stress and dynamic viscosity) as it is proposed by Shao and Lo [12].

$$\mu_{eff} = \frac{\mu_0 + \mu_\infty K_B \dot{\gamma}}{1 + K_B \dot{\gamma}} \tag{13}$$

with $K_B = \dfrac{\mu_0}{\tau_y}$, $\mu_\infty = \mu$ and $\mu_0 = 10^3 \mu$.

Assuming a vertical parabolic distribution for velocity u, $\dot{\gamma} = \dfrac{3\bar{u}}{H}$, the depth integrated stress term results in this case

$$S_{fx} = \frac{\mu_{eff} \dot{\gamma}}{\rho g H} + \frac{N^2 \bar{u}^2}{H^{4/3}} \tag{14}$$

To determine the viscosity μ and yield stress τ_y as a function of the volumetric sediment concentration, exponential formulas, as those given by O'Brien and Julien [11], are used:

$$\mu = \alpha_1 e^{\beta_1 \bar{c}} \tag{15}$$

$$\tau_y = \alpha_2 e^{\beta_2 \bar{c}} \tag{16}$$

For water-Kaolinite clay mixtures [8], α_1=0.621E-3, β_1=17.3, α_2=0.002 and β_2=34.2, μ is in Pa.s, τ_y is in Pa and $\bar{c}$ is a fraction of 1.

The shallow water equations and the sediment transport equation are solved by the Galerkin Finite Element method using three-node triangular elements. To solve the system of equations we propose a four-step time stepping scheme and a selective lumping method, as described by Garcia et al. [4]. This scheme improves previous finite elements models, allowing larger time steps and enhancing its capability to simulate complex debris flow events without requiring an artificial diffusion term. The use of triangular non structured grids gives the model a great flexibility to accommodate buildings and other obstacles usually present in urbanized alluvial fans.

3   Results

The first test problem represents flow from a source of finite size (area A and unit width), a dam break of mud-slide with initial triangular shape (height H_0 and length L_0) on a slope θ, as shown in Fig. 1. The fluid is a Kaolinite suspension with Cv=13.05% and the flow is considered unsteady, gradually varied, and laminar.

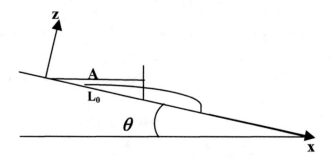

Figure 1:   One-dimensional dam break on a incline plane.

The finite element numerical solution is compared with the analytical solution proposed by Huang and Garcia [6, 7] and with experimental data given in their work. Although the example is one dimensional, 2D elements are used to discretize the channel using a 2D mesh.

Fig. 2 shows the spreading rate for the following conditions: θ=11°, and A=24.7cm^2 (L_0 = 0.16 m).These results show that the numerical solution using Cross model is in very good agreement with the experimental data for early stages of the solution, where the analytical solution is not as accurate. As time increases, the fluid velocity decreases but the stoppage of the fluid is not totally reached with the numerical solution. After a certain time, the numerical solution tends to increase and deviate from the analytical solution. This is probably caused by the numerical treatment of the dry-wet interface. Ongoing work is addressing this issue.

Fig. 3 shows free surface profiles obtained using Cross formulation. Two different meshes are used, in the new mesh (NM) elements are three times smaller than those in the old mesh (OM). In addition, the selective lumping parameter (related with the finite element solution of the governing equations) is increased from 0.925 to 0.950. As it is depicted in the figure, the mesh refinement contributes to reduce the numerical diffusion and improves substantially the solution in the advancing front. Increasing the selective lumping parameter also enhances the numerical solution, making it closer to the analytical solution.

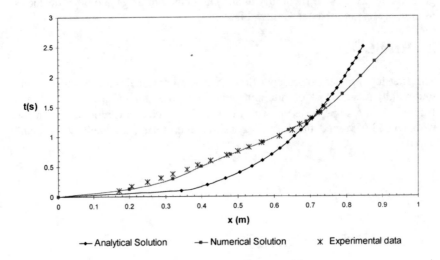

Figure 2: Spreading relation.

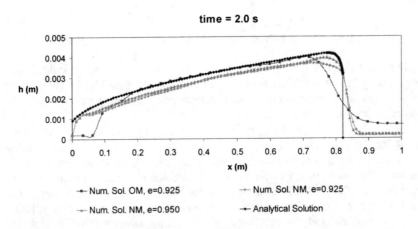

Figure 3: Free surface profiles.

Fig. 4 shows free surface profiles at time 2.3 s on wet slope, where a layer of fluid exists downstream from the mud-slide. The downstream layer has a height h2 equals to *0.5hy*, where *hy* is the so called yield depth defined by

$$hy = \frac{\tau_y}{\rho g \sin \theta} \tag{17}$$

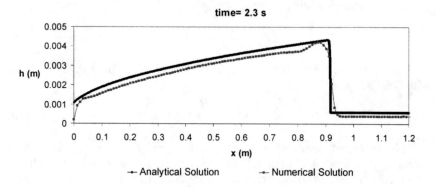

Figure 4:   Free surface profiles on wet slope.

The numerical solution obtained using Cross formulation is in very good agreement with the analytical solution [6].

Fig. 5 is a dimensionless plot of the wave shock depth (hf/H) as a function of the shock coordinate (xf/L), where H and L are the initial height and length of the triangular fluid source. The results are for $\lambda=0.04$, $\lambda=hy/L$, and for different values of $h2$ [6]. The numerical solution shows an accurate approximation of the analytical solution in all the cases.

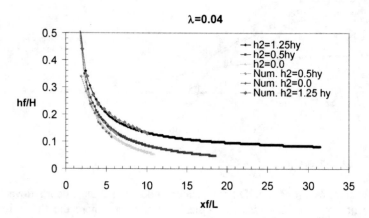

Figure 5:   Kinematic-wave shock depth plotted as function of shock coordinate.

Fig. 6 shows the analytical results of a circular dam break on a horizontal plane, presented by Balmforth et al. [1]. The initial condition of the problem is $h^*=h/H=1$ for $r^*=r/L\leq1$, where H and L are the initial height and radius of the circular, confined, source of fluid. The dimensionless time t^* is defined as

$$t^* = \frac{tL}{V} \tag{18}$$

where V is a characteristic velocity given by

$$V = \frac{\rho h H^3 \cos\theta}{\mu L}$$ (19)

The results are for a Bingham number (dimensionless yield stress) B=0.15, with B defined as

$$B = \frac{\tau_y H}{\mu V}$$ (20)

This analytical solution is compared with results given by the Cross formulation (numerical solution) for the same two-dimensional problem. Comparing curves, it is noticeable that the spreading of the numerical solution is larger than the analytical solution at advanced times; however, results are closer at short times.

Preliminary analysis leads us to attribute this behaviour to inaccuracies of the wetting and drying method used in the model, since this factors may play an increasingly important role for smaller depths. We are currently working on further model verifications and testing new wetting and drying algorithms to improve the model accuracy for large times.

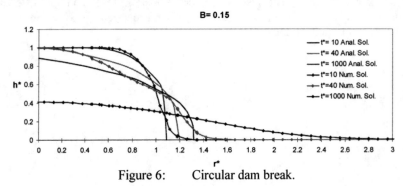

Figure 6:   Circular dam break.

4   Conclusions

In this paper, we propose a 2D finite element model to simulate debris flows based on the non-Newtonian Cross rheological formulation, where the fluid viscosity changes continuously from a finite value to a very high one (but much less than infinity) as the shear rate tends to zero. The 2D model is based on the shallow water equations, where the stress terms account for the bottom friction using Manning's formula and the internal friction losses are implemented using the Cross constitutive relations. The numerical method is based on a four-step, selective lumping, explicit time stepping scheme, that solves the system of ordinary differential equations that results from the discretization of the 2D shallow water equations. We present preliminary tests for one dimensional and two dimensional dam break problems, comparing the model results with some experimental data and analytical solutions.   Model results show very good agreement with the experimental data and analytical solutions in one dimensional cases. For the flow early stages, the numerical solution agrees better with the experimental data than with the analytical solution. However; in final stages, the numerical solution predicts that the fluid front advances more rapidly than the analytical solution and measured fluid front. The same results are observed in a 2D problem; however, experimental data to compare with is scarce. The proposed 2D debris flow model using Cross rheological formulation provides very stable results even in the range of very low shear rates, where other discontinuous constitutive relations that use the yield stress may become unstable.

References

[1] Balmforth, N. J., Craster, R. V., Rust, A.C. & Sassi, R. Viscoplastic flow over inclined surface. *Journal of Non-Newtonian Fluid Mechanics,* 139:103–127, 2006.
[2] Barnes, H.A., Hutton J.F. & Walters, K. *An introduction to rheology,* Elsevier: Amsterdam, 1989.
[3] Coussot, P. *Mudflow rheology and dynamics.* IAHR Monograph Series, Balkema, 1997.
[4] García-Martínez, R. Espinoza, E. Valera & M. González. An explicit two-dimensional finite element model to simulate short and long term bed evolution in alluvial rivers. *Journal of Hydraulic Research,* 44 (6): 2006.
[5] Hammad, K. & Vradis, G.C. Flow of a non-Newtonian Bingham plastic through an axisymmetric sudden contraction: effects of Reynolds and yield numbers. *Numerical Methods Non- Newtonian Fluid Dynamics,* ASME 179:63–90, 1994.
[6] Huang, X. & Garcia, M.H. Asymptotic solution for Bingham debris flows. *Debris Flow Hazards Mitigation,* ASCE, New York, 561–575, 1997.
[7] Huang, X. & Garcia, M.H. A Herschel-Bulkley model for mud flow down a slope. *Journal of Fluid Mechanics,* U. K., 374:305–333, 1998.
[8] Komatina, D. & Jomanovic, M. Experimental study of steady and unsteady free surface flows with water-clay mixtures. *Journal of Hydraulic Research,* 35:579–590, 1997.
[9] Martinez, C., F. Miralles-Wilhem and R. Garcia-Martinez. *A 2D finite element debris flow model based on the cross rheology formulation.* Fourth International Conference on Debris-Flow Hazards Mitigation: Mechanics, Prediction and Assessment. Chendu, China, September, 2007.
[10] O'Brien, J.S. and Julien, P.Y. Physical properties and mechanics of hyperconcentrated sediment flows. *ASCE Specialty Conference on the Delineation of Landslides, Floods and Debris Flows Hazards.* ASCE, New York, 260–279, 1985.
[11] O'Brien, J.S. & Julien, P.Y. Laboratory analysis of mudflows properties. *Journal of Hydraulic Engineering,* ASCE 114:877–887, 1988.
[12] Shao, S. & Lo, E.Y. Incompressible SPH method for simulating Newtonian and Non-Newtonian flows with a free surface. *Advances in Water Resources,* 26:787–800, 2003.

Numerical modelling of transient flows with high sediment concentrations

B. J. Dewals[1,2], S. Erpicum[1] & M. Pirotton[1]
[1]*Department ArGEnCo, University of Liege, Belgium*
[2]*Fund for Scientific Research F.R.S.-FNRS, Belgium*

Abstract

The main purpose of the present paper is to describe and discuss the development, validation and application of a numerical model designed to handle transient flows with high sediment transport rates. The model considers non-equilibrium transport (i.e. accounting for loading/unloading delay) and is numerically as well as physically totally coupled. The closure relations needed to evaluate the exchange fluxes between the fixed bottom and the flowing mixture (erosion and deposition rates) are also detailed in the paper. Finally, the model is validated against experimental data collected in the framework of the European project IMPACT.

Keywords: sediment transport, depth-averaged flow modelling, finite volume, erosion rate, dam break on an erodible topography.

1   Introduction

Conventional models for flow and sediment transport usually consider a weak numerical and physical coupling between the sub-models for hydrodynamics and for sediment transport. However, in numerous cases of intense transport conditions, such as debris flows but also flows caused by dam breaks occurring in erodible valleys, the above-mentioned loose coupling is not valid. In particular, many historical dam break events in the world are known to have induced highly erosive flows, which in turn caused significant scouring in the downstream valley, both in the floodplains and on other structures (e.g. dam breaching in cascade).

For the purpose of modelling such flows, characterized by extremely high sediment loads, the sub-models for hydrodynamics and sediment transport need

WIT Transactions on Engineering Sciences, Vol 60, © 2008 WIT Press
www.witpress.com, ISSN 1743-3533 (on-line)
doi:10.2495/DEB080081

to be tightly coupled both numerically and physically. The numerical coupling is necessary for the model to be able to handle properly regime changes and moving discontinuities (hydraulic jumps, sediment bores …), while it leads to genuine challenges in the development of suitable upwind discretization schemes and in terms of required computation time. The physical coupling implies that the momentum balance takes into consideration the effect of sediment concentration on the pressure distribution and on the inertia of the mixture.

In the present model, the momentum equations account explicitly for the concentration in sediments in the flow, hence tightly coupling the dynamics of water and of solid particles. Besides, the present model considers non-equilibrium transport (i.e. accounting for loading/unloading delay). The closure relations needed to evaluate the exchange fluxes between the fixed bottom and the flowing mixture (erosion and deposition rates) are also detailed in the paper, as well as the other main features of the model. Finally, the model is validated against experimental data collected in the framework of a European project.

2 Model description

The present model for flow and (equilibrium or non-equilibrium) sediment transport [6] has been entirely derived from the local conservation equations, by application of a depth-averaging operation, and doesn't simply result from a macroscopic approach. Subsection 2.1 presents the conservation laws, while the concentration profile is discussed in subsection 2.2 and the formulation of the diffusive terms in subsection 2.3. The closure relations required for evaluating the bed shear stress components, as well as the erosion and deposition rates, are detailed respectively in subsections 2.4 and 2.5.

2.1 Conservation laws

As detailed by Dewals [6], the model is based on two mass conservation equations, respectively for the water-sediment mixture and for the transported sediments:

$$\frac{\partial}{\partial t}\Big[h\big(1+\Delta s\overline{C}\big)\Big]+\frac{\partial}{\partial x}\Big[h\big(1+\Delta s\overline{C}\big)\overline{u}\Big]+\frac{\partial}{\partial y}\Big[h\big(1+\Delta s\overline{C}\big)\overline{v}\Big]=\Big[1+\Delta s\big(1-p\big)\Big]\frac{e_b}{1-p} \quad (1)$$

$$\frac{\partial}{\partial t}\big(h\overline{C}\big)+\frac{\partial}{\partial x}\big(h\overline{u}\overline{C}\big)+\frac{\partial}{\partial y}\big(h\overline{v}\overline{C}\big)=-\left[\frac{\partial}{\partial x}\left(h\frac{v_T}{\sigma_T}\frac{\partial\overline{C}}{\partial x}\right)+\frac{\partial}{\partial y}\left(h\frac{v_T}{\sigma_T}\frac{\partial\overline{C}}{\partial x}\right)\right]+e_b, \quad (2)$$

and two momentum equations, written for the water-sediment mixture:

$$\frac{\partial}{\partial t}\big(\rho_m h\overline{u}\big)+\frac{\partial}{\partial x}\big(\rho_m h\overline{u}^2\big)+\frac{\partial}{\partial y}\big(\rho_m h\overline{u}\overline{v}\big)+\frac{\partial}{\partial x}\left(\rho_m g\sin\theta_z\frac{h^2}{2}\right)+\rho_m hg\sin\theta_z\frac{\partial z_b}{\partial x}$$

$$=\rho_w\Big[1+\Delta s\big(1-p\big)\Big]\frac{e_b-|e_b|}{2\big(1-p\big)}\overline{u}\beta+\rho_m gh\sin\theta_x+\tau_{bx}+\frac{\partial h\overline{\sigma_x}}{\partial x}+\frac{\partial h\overline{\tau_{xy}}}{\partial y}, \quad (3)$$

and

$$\frac{\partial}{\partial t}\left(\rho_m h \overline{v}\right)+\frac{\partial}{\partial x}\left(\rho_m h \overline{u}\,\overline{v}\right)+\frac{\partial}{\partial y}\left(\rho_m h \overline{v}^2\right)+\frac{\partial}{\partial y}\left(\rho_m g \sin\theta_z \frac{h^2}{2}\right)+\rho_m g h \sin\theta_z \frac{\partial z_b}{\partial y}$$

$$=\rho_w\left[1+\Delta s(1-p)\right]\frac{e_b-\left|e_b\right|}{2(1-p)}\,\overline{v}\,\beta+\rho_m g h \sin\theta_y+\tau_{by}+\frac{\partial h\overline{\tau}_{xy}}{\partial x}+\frac{\partial h\overline{\sigma}_y}{\partial y}. \tag{4}$$

Besides, the evolution of the bed elevation is governed by the Exner equation:

$$\frac{\partial}{\partial t}\left[(1-p)z_b\right]+\frac{\partial q_{bx}}{\partial x}+\frac{\partial q_{by}}{\partial y}=-e_b. \tag{5}$$

The solid discharges q_{bx} and q_{by} may represent both equilibrium solid transport (such as bed load) and a gravity-induced contribution to the solid transport [6, 9].

The main symbols used above are defined in section 5. The following formulation for the density of the mixture has been exploited to derive the conservation equations (1)–(4):

$$\rho_m=\rho_w\left(1-C\right)+\rho_s C=\rho_w\left[1+(s-1)C\right]=\rho_w\left(1+\Delta s\,C\right). \tag{6}$$

Such a coupled approach is required for applications involving highly transient flows and high transport rates (e.g. induced by dam break and breaching), since in such cases the variation of the density of the water-sediment mixture may not be neglected [10].

The velocity profiles, as well as the profile of concentration along the depth of the flow, have been assumed to be uniform, as discussed hereafter. The evaluation of the bottom shear stress components τ_{bx} and τ_{by} is detailed in subsection 2.4.

Consistently with similar 1D formulations used by other authors, such as Capart [5], the source terms involving the erosion rate in equations (3) and (4) take non-zero values only in the case of deposition. The specific formulation used here is more comprehensively substantiated by Dewals [6]. In equations (3) and (4), β designates a correction factor accounting for the difference between the real velocity of sediments before deposition and the depth-averaged flow velocity.

The system of equations (1)–(5) constitutes a non-equilibrium two-dimensional extension to the model proposed by previous authors [5, 11, 12].

Of course, the system (1)–(5) becomes identical to a physically uncoupled model if $\Delta s\overline{C}$ is neglected compared to unity, which may be valid only for low sediment concentrations or for light solid particles.

The presently described mathematical and numerical model is incorporated in the modelling system "WOLF", developed at the University of Liege, which includes a process-oriented hydrological model, a 1D model for river networks as well as 2DH (depth-averaged) and 2DV hydrodynamic models.

2.2 Concentration and velocity profile

The theoretical "Rouse profile" is known to develop in a steady and uniform flow with low sediment concentration ($< 4\%$) [28], whereas the applications of the present model cover highly unsteady and non-uniform flows (e.g. dam break and dam breaching flows), for which the concentration profile deviates substantially from the conventional Rouse distribution. Since the real concentration profile remains extremely complex to characterize, a simple uniform distribution has been assumed, consistently with the definition of *mature* debris flows reported by Takahashi and Nakagawa [23].

Extending the previous assumption to a piecewise constant concentration profile, instead of a uniform one, would require only slight changes in the conservation equations (1)–(4). For instance, if the concentration is assumed to take the constant value C_b for $z_b \leq z \leq z_b + h_s$ (i.e. within a layer of thickness h_s), then $h\overline{C}$ in the equations simply needs to be replaced by $h_s C_b$ and the updated pressure term: $\left(h^2/2 + \Delta s\, C_b\, h_s^2/2\right) g \sin\theta_z$ must be used instead of the present one: $\left(1 + \Delta s\, \overline{C}\right) g \sin\theta_z \left(h^2/2\right)$. Several authors have used this assumption, typically keeping a constant value for C_b and calculating the time evolution of the thickness h_s [11, 12] or exploiting various empirical closure laws [17].

2.3 Diffusive terms

The diffusive terms in equations (2)–(4) may be neglected for most applications governed by highly advective processes, such as flows induced by dam breaks (see section 3). On the contrary, these terms would play a significant part for other applications, such as, for instance, the prediction of sediment deposition patterns in slower flow conditions. In such conditions, the turbulent diffusion terms need to be evaluated. Therefore, the depth-averaged Reynolds stresses $\overline{\sigma}_x$, $\overline{\sigma}_y$ and $\overline{\tau}_{xy}$ are expressed following the Boussineq's approximation (transposed for a depth-averaged model) [2, 20]:

$$\frac{\overline{\sigma}_x}{\rho} = 2\left(\nu + \nu_T\right)\frac{\partial \overline{u}}{\partial x}, \qquad \frac{\overline{\sigma}_y}{\rho} = 2\left(\nu + \nu_T\right)\frac{\partial \overline{v}}{\partial y}, \qquad \frac{\overline{\tau}_{xy}}{\rho} = \left(\nu + \nu_T\right)\left(\frac{\partial \overline{u}}{\partial y} + \frac{\partial \overline{v}}{\partial x}\right), \quad (7)$$

where ν represents the molecular kinematic viscosity, while the eddy viscosity ν_T is computed by a turbulence closure model ($\nu \ll \nu_T$), such as for instance the depth-averaged k-ε model developed by Erpicum [7, 8].

Besides, the diffusive terms in equation (2) have been expressed according to a Fick law, involving the Schmidt number σ_T, which usually varies in the range 0.5 to 1 [27] and may be reasonably approached by $\sigma_T = 0.5$ [9].

2.4 Closure relation for bed shear stress

The bed shear stress evaluation is also influenced by the presence of sediments in the flow, modifying the density of the fluid. According to Takahashi (1991), as reported by Leal *et al.* [17], the bed shear stress in equations (3) and (4)may be expressed by:

$$\frac{\tau_{bx}}{\rho_w} = -g\sin\theta_z\, h\big(1+\Delta s\overline{C}\big)J_x \quad \text{and} \quad \frac{\tau_{by}}{\rho_w} = -g\sin\theta_z\, h\big(1+\Delta s\overline{C}\big)J_y \qquad (8)$$

where J_x and J_y are the friction slopes calculated by an empirical friction law, such as the Manning formula. Relations (8) are also consistent with the approach used by Valiani and Caleffi [24]. Other more complex formulations are possible as well [3, 23].

2.5 Closure relations for erosion and deposition rates

Evaluating the net erosion rate e_b, equal to the erosion rate E minus the deposition rate D, is a key step in the modelling procedure, since all exchanges between the flow layer and the erodible bottom are governed by this parameter. Among various possible approaches [9, 13, 15, 18, 19, 21, 25, 26], a simple *reaction equation* is used here, assuming that e_b is proportional to the difference between the instantaneous concentration value $\overline{C}$ and the equilibrium concentration $\overline{C}_*$ [4, 24]:

$$e_b = E - D = -\frac{\omega_s}{\Lambda}\big(\overline{C}-\overline{C}_*\big), \qquad (9)$$

where ω_s represents the settling velocity and Λ is a non-dimensional adaptation length, which may be approximated by means of semi-empirical relations [1,14].

3   Model validation: dam break flow on an erodible bed

The model depicted above has been validated by comparison with measured data of an idealized dam break experiment on an erodible topography. The experiments were carried out as a benchmark for validation of numerical codes in the framework of the EU research project IMPACT [16, 22].

3.1 Description of the benchmark

The idealized dam break experiments were undertaken in a 2.5 m long and 10 cm wide laboratory flume. The bottom of the channel is initially horizontal and consists of a layer of non-cohesive sediments. The solid particles are PVC grains, characterized by a mean diameter of 3 mm and a relative density of 1.54.

Initially, a sluice gate defines two distinct zones in the channel. Upstream of the gate, a 10 cm-deep volume of water is at rest, while downstream of the gate, the water level is set at the same level as the surface of the sediment layer, thus completely saturating the erodible bed with water. At the beginning of the experiment, the sluice gate is raised quickly. This operation of opening is achieved within less than 50 ms, so that it may be assumed to be instantaneous in the numerical modelling.

3.2 Simulation parameters

The simulation domain is discretized with 500 cells of 5 mm each. The time integration is conducted based on an explicit two-step Runge-Kutta scheme, leading to a second order accuracy.

As a results of the extreme transport rates expected to be induced by the dam break flow, the transport capacity formula, used to determine the equilibrium concentration in sediments, is expressed as a function of the *mobility parameter* $\theta = u/\sqrt{g(s-1)d}$, which characterizes the behaviour of such debris flows [5].

Therefore, the amount of solid materials transported at equilibrium is assumed to be given by a power law of this mobility parameter: $h\overline{C}_* = k\theta^m$, where m represents the power of the transport capacity formula, while k designates the coefficient of the formula.

The simulations are based on the following values of the parameters involved in the transport capacity law: $k = 10^{-3}$ and $m = 3$, while the non-dimensional adaptation length Λ is simply supposed to be unity. Two different friction coefficients have been tested ($n = 0.01$ m/s and $n = 0.02$ m/s), in order to appreciate the sensitivity of the flow and transport rate with respect to the roughness parameter.

3.3 Results and discussion

Figure 1 displays the free surface and bottom elevation profiles at four successive times following the idealized dam break: 0.25 s, 0.50 s, 0.75 s and

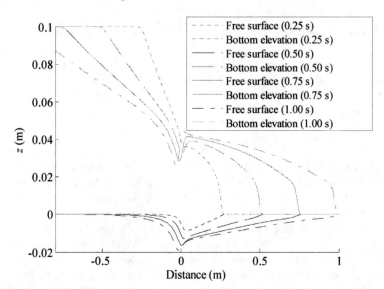

Figure 1:   Free surface and bottom elevation profiles at four successive instants following the idealized dam break.

1.00 s. Figure 2 represents the time evolution of the free surface elevation and the bed level, both measured during the experiments and simulated with the present model. The results are provided at three points situated respectively at 25 cm, 50 cm and 75 cm downstream of the initial location of the sluice gate.

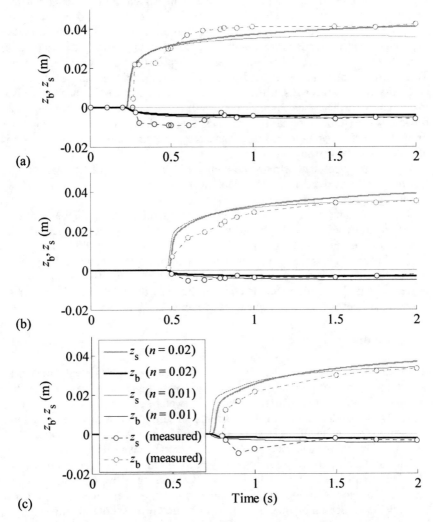

Figure 2:   Simulated vs measured time evolution of the bottom elevation and the free surface at the abscissa (a) 0.25 m, (b) 0.50 m, (c) 0.75 m. Comparison of the simulated results for two different roughness coefficients, namely $n = 0.01$ and 0.02 s/m$^{1/3}$.

Figure 2 reveals that the time of arrival of the front is reproduced with a relatively high accuracy. The run based on the higher friction coefficient also succeeds in predicting the water level with a reasonable accuracy, while the final scouring depth is reproduced satisfactorily as well. On the other hand, the simulated time evolution of the bottom elevation is monotonous, whereas experimental data reveals intense scouring at the very beginning of the test, followed by an increase in the bottom elevation. This discrepancy results most probably from significant vertical components of velocity in the vicinity of the initial location of the sluice gate. Such vertical velocity components are not considered in the present depth-averaged numerical model. In addition, the experimental measurements are inevitably affected by local errors, especially due to the highly unsteady biphasic flow and transport processes considered here. Those errors remain however hard to quantify close to the initial gate location since the flow is most disturbed in this area and its erosive capacity is also maximum there. The increase in two steps in the measured free surface level is obviously linked to the scouring dynamics. The prediction of the time evolution of the free surface would hence be enhanced by a better simulation of the erosion effects during the first instants.

Figure 2(b) also demonstrates the ability of the model to predict realistically the time of arrival of the front. Moreover, this result shows a rather low sensitivity with respect to the friction coefficient.

The maximum free surface elevation is better reproduced on the basis of the lower friction coefficient. In this respect, the model would advantageously be enhanced by using a formulation of friction law more specifically dedicated to debris flows. In Figure 2(c), the simulated time of arrival of the front appears underestimated, whereas the maximum free surface elevation tends to be overestimated. These observations confirm the need for an enhanced modelling of energy dissipation, possibly considering explicitly the transport rate.

4 Conclusion

A model has been presented to simulate flows with sediment transport, potentially in highly unsteady conditions and with high transport rates. In the momentum balance, the density of the fluid (water-sediment mixture) depends explicitly on the concentration in sediments, ensuring thus a physical coupling between the dynamics of water and sediments. The required closure relations for evaluating the bottom shear stress and the erosion rate have been described.

For validation purpose, the model has been tested against experimental data of a benchmark involving highly erosive flows induced by an idealized dam break on a mobile topography. A satisfactory agreement has been shown between the numerical prediction and the measured results, both in terms of free surface elevation and time of arrival of the front.

5 Symbols

$\bar{C}$	depth-averaged concentration	[-]
e_b	net volumic erosion rate	[m/s]
h	water depth	[m]

p	bed porosity	[-]
q_{bx}, q_{by}	solid discharge (bed load and gravity-induced)	[m²/s]
s	relative density of the sediments: $s = \rho_s / \rho_w$ ($\Delta s = s - 1$)	[-]
t	time	[s]
$\bar{u}$, $\bar{v}$	depth-averaged velocity components along x and y	[m/s]
x, y	space coordinates along the reference axes	[m]
z_b	bed elevation	[m]
θ_x, θ_y, θ_z	angle between the reference axes and the vertical direction	[-]
ρ_w, ρ_s, ρ_m	density of, respectively, water, sediments and the mixture	[m³/s]
τ_{bx}, τ_{by}	bottom shear stress along x and y	[N/m²]

References

[1] Armanini, A. and G.D. Silvio, *A one-dimensional model for the transport of a sediment mixture in non-equilibrium conditions.* J. Hydraul. Res., 1988. **26**(3): p. 275–292.

[2] ASCE Task Committee on Turbulence Models in Hydraulic Computations, *Turbulence modeling of surface water flow and transport: Part I.* J. Hydraul. Eng.-ASCE, 1988. **114**(9): p. 970–991.

[3] Brufau, P., P. Garcia-Navarro, P. Ghilardi, L. Natale and F. Savi, *1D mathematical modelling of debris flow.* J. Hydraul. Res., 2000. **38**(6): p. 435.

[4] Caleffi, V. and A. Valiani. *A mathematical model for dam-break over movable bed.* in *Proc. 1st Int. Conf. on Fluvial Hydraulics: River Flow 2002, Louvain-la-Neuve, Belgium, 4-6 September 2002.* 2002. Roterdam: Balkema.

[5] Capart, H., *Dam-break induced geomorphic flows and the transitions from solid- to fluid-like behaviour across evolving interfaces.* 2000, PhD thesis, Université catholique de Louvain: 208 p.

[6] Dewals, B., *Une approche unifiée pour la modélisation d'écoulements à surface libre, de leur effet érosif sur une structure et de leur interaction avec divers constituants.* 2006, PhD thesis, University of Liege: 636 p.

[7] Dewals, B.J., S.A. Kantoush, S. Erpicum, M. Pirotton and A.J. Schleiss, *Experimental and numerical analysis of flow instabilities in rectangular shallow basins.* Environ. Fluid Mech., 2008 (published on-line).

[8] Erpicum, S., *Optimisation objective de paramètres en écoulements turbulents à surface libre sur maillage multibloc.* 2006, PhD thesis, University of Liege.

[9] Fäh, R., *Numerische Simulation der Strömung in offenen Gerinnen mit beweglicher Sohle.* Mitteilungen der Versuchsanstalt für Wasserbau, Hydrologie un Glaziologie, ed. D. Vischer. Vol. 153. 1997, Zürich: ETHZ, 161 p.

[10] Fraccarollo, L. and A. Armanini. *A semi-analytical solution for the dam-break problem over a movable bed.* in *Proc. XXVIII IAHR Congress.* 1999. Graz, Austria.

[11] Fraccarollo, L. and H. Capart, *Riemann wave description of erosional dam-break flows*. J. Fluid Mech., 2002. **461**: p. 183–228.

[12] Fraccarollo, L., H. Capart and Y. Zech, *A Godunov method for the computation of erosional shallow water transients*. Int. J. Numer. Meth. Fluids, 2003. **41**: p. 951.

[13] Froehlich, D.C. *IMPACT Project field tests 1 and 2: "blind" simulation by DaveF*. in *2nd IMPACT Project Workshop*. 2002. Mo-i-Rana, Norway.

[14] Galappatti, G. and C.B. Vreugdenhil, *A depth-integrated model for suspended sediment transport*. J. Hydraul. Res., 1985. **23**(4): p. 359–375.

[15] Köngeter, J. and C. Forkel, *Vorlesungsumdruck Hydromechanik III*. 2000: Aachen University of Technology, 128 p.

[16] Leal, J., R. Ferreira, A. Cardoso and A. Almeida. *Overview of IST Group Results on the Sediment Benchmark*. in *Proc. 3rd IMPACT Project Workshop*. 2003. Louvain-la-Neuve, Belgium.

[17] Leal, J.G.A.B., R.M.L. Ferreira and A.H. Cardoso, *Dam-break wave propagation over a cohesionless erodible bed*, in *Proc. 30th IAHR Congress*, J. Ganoulis and P. Prinos (eds). Vol. C. 2003, IAHR: Thessaloniki. p. 261–268.

[18] Mercier, C., *Modélisation tridimensionnelle du transport sédimentaire au large de la côte belge*. 2004, Diploma thesis, University of Liege: 75 p.

[19] Paquier, A. *Sediment transport models used by Cemagref during Impact project*. in *Proc. 1st IMPACT Project Workshop*. 2002. Wallingford, UK.

[20] Rodi, W., *Turbulence models and their application in hydraulics - A state-of-the-art (second revised edition)*. 1984: Balkema.

[21] Singh, V., *Dam breach modeling technology*. Water Science and Technology Library. 1996, Dordecht, Bos, London: Kluwer Academic Publishers, 242 p.

[22] Spinewine, B. and Y. Zech. *Dam-break waves over movable beds: a "flat bed" test case*. in *Proc. 2nd IMPACT Project Workshop*. 2002. Mo-I-Rana, Norway.

[23] Takahashi, T. and H. Nakagawa, *Flood/debris flow hydrograph due to collapse of a natural dam by overtopping*. Journal of Hydroscience and Hydraulic Engineering, Japan Society of Civil Engineers, JSCE, 1994. **12**(2): p. 41–49.

[24] Valiani, A. and V. Caleffi. *Dam break modelling for sediment laden flows*. in *Int. Symp. on Environmental Hydraulics*. 2001. Arizona State University, USA.

[25] van Rijn, L.C., *Sediment transport, Part II: suspended load Transport*. J. Hydraul. Eng.-ASCE, 1984. **110**(11): p. 1613–1641.

[26] van Rijn, L.C., *Sediment pick-up functions*. J. Hydraul. Eng.-ASCE, 1984. **110**(10): p. 1494–1502.

[27] Wang, S.S.Y. and W. Wu. *River sedimentation and morphology modeling - The state of the art and future development*. in *Proc. 9th Int. Symposium on River Sedimentation*. 2004. Yichang, China.

[28] Woo, H.S., P.Y. Julien and E.V. Richardson, *Suspension of large Concentrations of Sands*. J. Hydraul. Eng.-ASCE, 1988. **114**(8): p. 888–898.

Debris flow modelling in Julian Alps using FLO-2D

C. Calligaris, M. A. Boniello & L. Zini
*Department of Geological, Environmental and Marine Sciences,
Trieste University, Italy*

Abstract

Val Canale Valley is located in the Italian Julian Alps, in the north-eastern corner of Friuli Venezia Giulia Region. On 29 August 2003, the area has been invested by a strong intensity meteorological event (rainfall maxima from Pontebba station, which recorded the highest rainfall depths, were characterised by return periods in the range of 500–1000 years for 3-h, 6-h and 12-h periods) that caused debris flow phenomena. These have damaged infrastructures and killed people. In collaboration with the Geological Service of Friuli Venezia Giulia Region and with the contribution, for the input data, of the Department of Territory and Sour-Forest Systems of the University of Padova, we investigated twelve river basins located in the studied valley with different geological-geomorphological characteristics. The main objective of the study is to model the debris flow phenomena. This goal has been obtained using FLO-2D software. In all the basins implicated, we have collected samples for grain size curve distributions and rheological analyses in order to characterize the detrital material. First of all it has been necessary to execute a back analysis study with the aim of better define all the parameters involved. Subsequently, the goal has been to simulate a new alluvional event with a return time of 200 years, on the basis of actual morphology obtained from laser scan data (where data have been available) realizing a DEM based on a grid cell size of 5 m. On this topographic base it has been possible to insert the defence infrastructures realized after the alluvional event. From all this input data it has been possible to model and to simulate the potential debris flow with the aim to obtain, vulnerability first, and hazard mapping later, necessary for the future territorial planning.

Keywords: debris flow, FLO-2D, mitigating measures, Alps, territorial planning.

WIT Transactions on Engineering Sciences, Vol 60, © 2008 WIT Press
www.witpress.com, ISSN 1743-3533 (on-line)
doi:10.2495/DEB080091

1   Introduction

During the last 20 years, in the alpine region, several severe meteorological events have caused debris flow phenomena that have damaged the infrastructures causing problems to the tourist economy of the involved areas (Tropeano et al. [1]). The study area, Val Canale, is a north-east oriented valley located in the north-eastern part of Italy. The area is of a great interest from a geological point of view because of different formations interested by faults and structural dislocations, elevated slopes and a high rate of urbanization considering that it is an highly seismic mountain area . All these factors induced the researchers of the University of Trieste (Department of Geological, Environmental and Marine Sciences) to consider the area as a good test site for simulate, with FLO-2D, a scenario of debris flow phenomena with a return time of 200 years. FLO-2D software is based on a quadratic shear stress model (O'Brien and Julien [2]) and it is considered the most appropriate modelling software to describe the continuum of flow regimes from viscous to turbulent/dispersive flows (Tecca et al. [3]). We presents numerical modelling of 12 debris flow events already occurred that with their sediment loads remarkable property damages. As a first step it has been necessary to calibrate the software using field data (references documentation, geological surveys and grain size analyses) to realize 12 back-analyses for every single basin. As second step, the parameter values obtained from back-analysis have been inserted in the software and it has been possible to define future flow directions. To complete the study it has been necessary to consider the mitigation works in order to better understand the possible directions of the flow in a potential future event. This is very useful tool for future planning for all the local Authorities.

2   Description of the main flood event

The area of Val Canale, Canal del Ferro and Val Aupa, as well as the entire part of the north-eastern Friuli Venezia Giulia Region, was interested by a high intensity rainfall on the 29th August 2003. The rainfall started at 12 a.m., firstly affecting the upper sector of the mountain areas among Cucco, Malborghetto and Ugovizza villages, then it gradually moved downwards with increasing intensity. A total of 293 mm of rainfall was recorded by the Pontebba pluviometric station from 2 to 6 p.m. The rainfall and associated debris flow events 29th August 2003 caused the death of two persons, 300 displaced and 260 damaged houses and it caused substantial damages to infrastructures that were made unavailable for several days. The mobilization of more than a thousand of landslides occurred along the studies sides. Hydrological analyses were performed using data recorded by Pontebba rain-gage. This instrument is part of the network managed by the Regional Directorate of Civil Defence. Data are available at an interval time of 30 minutes. Maximum values of 50,8 mm in 30 minutes (between 5 and 5.30 p.m.), 88.6 mm per hour (from 3.30 to 4.30 p.m), 233.4 mm in three hours (between 2.30 and 5.30 p.m.) and 343.0 in six hours (from 12 a.m. to 6 p.m.) were observed. The total influx of meteoric event, which lasted about 12 hours, was equal to 389.6 mm. Regarding the payback time characterizing the event, there is a considerable variation dependent on the duration: between 1 and 24 hours, the time of delivery is between 50 and 100 years; for 12 hours it is between 200 and 500 years, while, for a period from 3 to 6 hours, payback time varies between 500 and 1000 years (Borga et al. [4]).

3 Geological framework

In the complexity of the event just described, twelve basins have been chosen from the local authorities to be studied. These basins are located in Val Canale valley and in smaller valleys next to it (Fig.1).

Figure 1:   Area location.

The litostratigraphical units in the studied area are essentially represented by carbonate sedimentary units chronologically dated between Permian and Triassic often covered by loose recent deposits of Quaternary. Permian sediments are characterized by the Bellerophon Unit in which it is possible to associate dolomite and black limestones thickly stratified, that outcrops in the lower part of the valley. Triassic heterogeneous calcareous-terrigenus series (very stratified limestones and siltstones) made up the Werfen Unit. The Serla Unit overlaid the Werfen Unit being in direct tectonical contact. Serla is mainly composed of massive dolomite, dolomitic limestone, and less commonly by stratified limestones. Quaternary deposits are mostly represented in the lower part of the valley. According to their genesis, the deposits can be distinguished as gravitative, as detritical fans or screes, and deposits due to fluvial processes. Glacial deposits outcropping in different areas and having different stratigraphical positions are present in the entire studied area.

From a structural point of view, the tectonic features affecting the portion of territory are linked to the alpine orogeny and they are marked by wide monoclinal structures separated by east-west tectonic relocations. In the southern part of the investigated area, the monoclinal setting is affected from a regional displacing line called "Fella Sava", which has led the monoclinalic block to overtrust on a similar southernmost block. From the geomechanical point of view, stress associated with bending and faults have generated intense fracturation in the bedrock. The area is subjected to high seismicity and it is active from a tectonical point of view.

4   The numerical simulation

4.1   FLO-2D model

FLO-2D is a 2-dimensional flood routing model of volume conservation that routes a flood hydrograph while predicting floodwave attenuation due to flood storage. Hyperconcentrated sediment flow is simulated by the FLO-2D model using a quadratic rheological model that includes viscous stress, yield stress, turbulence and dispersive stress terms as a function of sediment concentration. The model uses the full dynamic wave momentum equation and a central finite difference routing scheme with eight potential flow directions to predict the progression of a flood hydrograph over a system of square grid elements. Wave propagation is fully controlled by topography and roughness or resistance to flow. The model is suitable to simulate flooding of rivers and can also be used to analyze problems of flood flows as unconventional not confined on alluvial fan with complex topography, mud flow and debris flow, and floods event affecting urban areas (FLO-2D [5]). The FLO-2D model is an effective tool for the evaluation of hazard floods event and planning for mitigation measures, for this reason it has been decided to use it to analyze what happened and what could happen in the future.

4.2   Software calibration through back analyses using twelve basins

In order to simulate with good precision, both the flooded area and the thickness of debris deposits, for all the twelve basins, the catastrophic event has been replicated. These back analyses have permitted to calibrate the parameters involved in the simulations and to characterize every single debris flow. To obtain this, first of all, it has been necessary to evaluate the topographical settings consisting in information layers contained in the Regional Technical Numerical Chart supplied by Friuli Venezia Giulia Region at a scale of 1:5000. From this data it was possible to obtain a DTM with a cell size of 5x5m. The DTM was imported in the FLO-2D pre-processor GDS and in this environment it has been created a computational domain having cell size of 5x5m. The topography was verified and corrected where possible, in particular it was necessary to change the elevation of roads, houses and, generally, of all infrastructures. This permitted to have a DTM as similar as possible to realty. One of the most paramount input parameters, important as a good topographical base, was the inflow hydrograph. Data were studied in collaboration with the Department of Territory and Agro-Forestry Systems of the University of Padova. This has permitted the creation of a single hydrograph for each of the twelve studied basins. For every single basin a different sediment concentration by volume was assigned to the hydrograph. The range has been between 0.2 as a minimum and 0.60 corresponding to a mature flow. The Manning coefficient used was 0.1 (Tecca et al. [3]). The resistance parameter for laminar flow K was assumed among 24, 1000 and 2285 suggested values for debris flow (D'Agostino and Tecca [7]). Rheological parameters were mainly obtained from the literature (FLO-2D [5]). It has been possible to identify twelve pairs of potential rheological parameters (Table 1), and therefore twelve simulations were consequently performed for every single basin. A model is successfully calibrated when the simulation results are consistent with the observed flow behaviour in terms of extent of flooded area, runout distance, estimate of deposited sediment volume and flow depth (cfr D'Agostino). Among the twelve simulations, for each basin the most suitable has been chosen.

Table 1:   Rheological parameters.

Simulations (back analysis)	η		τ		Model used
Name of basin	α	β	α	β	
Simulation 01	0.036	22.1	0.181	25.7	Aspen Pit 1
Simulation 02	0.0538	14.5	2.72	10.4	Aspen Pit 2
Simulation 03	0.00136	28.4	0.152	18.7	Aspen Natural Soil
Simulation 04	0.128	12	0.0473	21.1	Aspen Mine Fill
Simulation 05	0.000495	27.1	0.0383	19.6	Aspen Watershed
Simulation 06	0.000201	33.1	0.291	14.3	Aspen Mine Source Area
Simulation 07	0.00283	23	0.0345	20.1	Glenwood 1
Simulation 08	0.0648	6.2	0.0765	16.9	Glenwood 2
Simulation 09	0.00632	19.9	0.000707	29.8	Glenwood 3
Simulation 10	0.000602	33.1	0.00172	29.5	Glenwood 4
Simulation 11	0.0075	14.39	2.6	17.48	Dai et. al (1980)
Simulation 12	0.0075	14.39	0.152	18.7	Tecca et al.

4.3 Prediction of debris flow hazard

To use the results obtained whit the simulations as an useful tool for future planning for all the local Authorities, there has been the necessity to introduce, into the models the actual morphology and the mitigation structures already realized. New DTM were created using, where possible, laser scan data, and new structures, as depositional square, check dam, selective check dam, channels, river protection works and berms, were introduced manually, where necessary, into the GSD pre-processor module. To run the model, for each single basin, it was used the yield stress and the viscosity parameters obtained with the back analysis.

5   Final remarks

The application of the FLO-2D software to this kind of processes can improve the capability to predict debris flow behaviour and estimates depths and velocity, identify areas of inundation delineating hazard maps and design measures for hazard mitigations (Fig. 2 and Fig. 3) (Tecca et al. [3]). It is important to understand the conduct of the phenomena, in order to create several scenarios

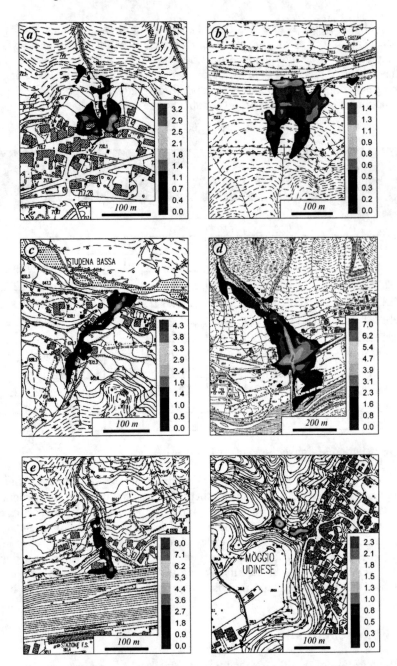

Figure 2:   Final flow depth areas calculated for basins:a) Malborghetto
Centro, b) Fella sinistra, c) Rio Ruscis, d) Rio Cucco, e) Rio
Pontebba 1, f) Moggio Udinese.

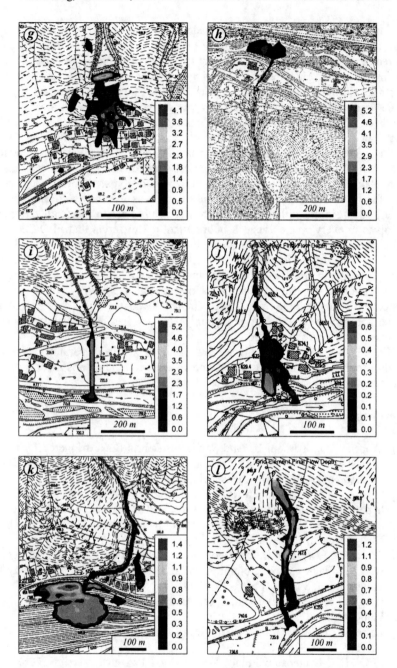

Figure 3:   Final flow depth areas calculated for basins: g) Abitato Cucco, h) Rio Pirgler, i) Malborghetto nuovo, j) Studena Bassa, k) Rio Pontebba 2, l) Malborghetto Est.

of a future event. In the simulations made it has been noticed that DTM starting data are really important. Morphology of the invested area has to be perfectly recreated, otherwise the flow could reach zones that have not been invested during the event. This means that having available laser scanner data is a good starting point for an accurate simulation. This appeared more important on small scale basins like the ones available for this study. The maximum area involved has been of about 1,66 km^2 (Rio Pirgler). Going on with the project, there has been several problems connected to the concentration by volume. In some basins, where the erosion has been substantial, many difficulties run up against calibrating the model in order to recreate the total volume stored on the floodplain. In the beginning, between the volume estimated during the surveys and the one obtained with the software there was a remarkable discrepancy. Later, adding more inflow points, it has been possible to insert all the debris involved in every single event. It is important not to forget that FLO-2D is not simulating the erosion (if you activate the mud/debris modality), so the flow is not increasing during its course, but it is only moving along the floodplain. For two of the twelve basins, during the simulations, we had a different approach. After the alluvial event of 1996, a lot of material has been removed, and the concentration by volume used for the simulation was too high (peak at 0.6), too much debris was flowing. A reduction in the Cv has been necessary just to increase the liquidity of the flow.

Concluding, every single phenomena has to be studied separately, according to its geological, geomorphological and rheological characteristics in order to reach a good consistency with the field data.

References

[1] Tropeano D., Turconi L., and Sanna S., Debris flows triggered by the 29 August 2003 cloudburst in Val Canale, eastern Italian Alps. Proc. Int. Symp. INTERPRAEVENT 2004, Riva del Garda, Italy, 2004.

[2] O'Brien J.S. and Julien P.Y., Physical properties and mechanics of hyperconcentrated sediment flows. Proc. ASCE Spec. Conf. on Delineation of Landslides, Flash Floods and Debris Flow Hazards in Utah, University of Utah at Logan, Utah, pp.260–279, 1985.

[3] Tecca P.R., Armento C. and Genevois R., Debris flow hazard and mitigation works in Fiames slope (Dolomites, Italy). WIT Transactions on Ecology and Environment, Vol. 90, pp.15–25, 2006.

[4] Borga et al., Hydrometeorological Analysis of the 29 August 2003 Flash Flood in the

[5] Eastern Italian Alps, American Meteorological Society, DOI: 10.1175/JHM593.1, 2007

[6] FLO-2D, 2-Dimensional Flood Routine Model Manual, Version 2006.

[7] D'Agostino V., Tecca P.R., Some considerations on the application of the FLO-2D model for debris flow hazard assessment, Monitoring, Simulations, Prevention and Remediation of Dense and Debris Flows, WIT Transactions on Ecology and Environment, Vol. 90, pp. 159–170, 2006.

Predicting debris flow susceptible areas through GIS modelling in Aparados da Serra (Brazil)

A. J. Strieder[1], S. A. Buffon[2], T. F. P. de Quadros[3]
& H. R. Oliveira[4]
[1]Lab. Modelagem Geológica e Ambiental, MODELAGE-UFRGS, Brazil
[2]Ministério Público do Rio Grande do Sul, DAT-MP-RS, Brazil
[3]Departamento Nacional da Produção Mineral, DNPM, Brazil
[4]Transportadora Gasoduto Bolívia-Brasil S.A., TBG-Sul, Brazil

Abstract

This paper aims to present the results of a GIS modelling to predict debris flow susceptible areas in the Aparados da Serra region (Brazil). The region shows a 1000 m high scarp located close to Atlantic Ocean in southern Brazil. The scarp is developed upon sandstones (Botucatu Fm.) and basalts and dacites (Serra Geral Fm.) of the Paraná Basin, after the break-up of the Gondwana Supercontinent and the opening of the South Atlantic Ocean. It is a topographic barrier to convective clouds migrating from ocean to the continent, mainly in spring and summer seasons. Geologic, geomorphologic, geotechnical mapping were conducted in order to enable GIS data modelling for debris flow in the region. The prediction of areas susceptible to debris flow along the scarp was based upon USPED algorithms. However, some changes were introduced into USPED algorithms in order to model debris flows in this region. The GIS modelling results distinguished susceptible areas for erosion and deposition of the debris, according the modified USPED procedures. These results were compared with a large debris flow event occurred in December 1995, and also recent small scale and localized debris flow events. All these observed debris flows show good correlation with predicted area of occurrence. Thus, it can be concluded that such GIS modelling can be applied to predict areas susceptible for erosion and deposition of debris related to concentrated convective storms.
Keywords: debris flows susceptibility map, GIS modelling, USPED, erosion and deposition.

WIT Transactions on Engineering Sciences, Vol 60, © 2008 WIT Press
www.witpress.com, ISSN 1743-3533 (on-line)
doi:10.2495/DEB080101

1 Introduction

Debris flows are hazardous natural mass movement processes that occur in many countries under different conditions. They are usually seen as a continuum from water flood, through hyper concentrated flow, to debris flow, and tend to flow down slope along channels or stream valleys [1]. Debris flows can be initiated when unconsolidated materials become unstable due to saturation by water, steepening of slopes by erosion or constructions, earthquake shaking, and volcanic eruptions. The water for the debris flows can be supplied by intense rainstorms, by melting of snow or ice, or by overflow of lakes.

Debris flow susceptibility maps have been produced in a number of ways [e.g. 2,3]. Susceptibility maps usually answer one of three important questions when dealing with debris flow: where debris flows will occur? Digital elevation models, geologic and historical data are used to define susceptible source and deposition areas. The complex number of physical parameters governing debris flow triggering makes susceptibility maps generation a difficult task. In some regions, the lack of historical data is an additional problem.

This paper aims to present the application of a modified USPED algorithm to predict source and deposition areas of debris flow. The USPED algorithm [4] includes almost the same physical parameters considered in debris flows. The result is a map distinguishing the relative susceptibility for debris flow source and deposition areas during intense tropical rainstorms (Aparados da Serra region, southern Brazil, fig. 1).

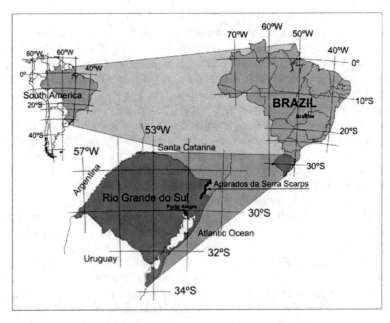

Figure 1:   Regional map locating Aparados da Serra region, southern Brazil.

2   Historical data in the Aparados da Serra region (Brazil)

The Aparados da Serra region lacks adequate historical data records for debris flow events. There exist some old reports in regional newspapers showing consequences of water floods, hyperconcentrated flows, and debris flows. The most recent and well documented event occurred in December 24th, 1995 (Figure 2). Pellerin *et al.* [5] described that December, 1995 showed very low precipitation and high temperature (La Niña event in southern Brazil). In these conditions, a fourth polar front migrated from Argentina, Uruguay and southern Brazil, acting mainly over the continent. Stratified clouds were responsible for widespread, low intensity precipitation. However, low altitude (± 600 m) cumulonimbus clouds migrated from the Atlantic Ocean toward the Aparados da Serra scarps (± 1200 m altitude). This resulted in concentrated, high intensity rainstorms. The records show precipitations as high as 400 mm for 24 hours period. Those records do not measure lower periods of time; but, it is known that the main part of that precipitation were established in periods less than 1-2 hours.

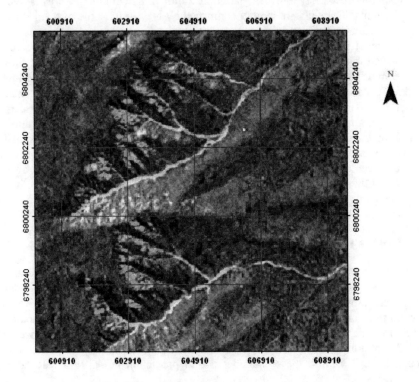

Figure 2:   LANDSAT image showing the location of the 24th December, 1995 debris flow event in Aparados da Serra region. The image results from (RGB composition TM5-97B1/TM5-94B1 : TM5-97B1 : TM5-94B1). Clear areas represent the December 1995 debris flow erosion and deposition.

Recent localized debris flow events (e.g. February, 2003, 2006 and January, 2008) were also related to large periods of very low precipitation and high temperature. The magnitude and intensity of such events are still being investigated.

3 Debris flow model for Aparados da Serra region (Brazil)

The geologic-geomorphologic model for triggering the debris flows were developed based on geological mapping, digital terrain modelling and geotechnical soil and vegetation mapping. The model also incorporates the precipitation regime for the Aparados da Serra region.

The Aparados da Serra scarp is mainly developed upon sandstones (Botucatu Fm.) and basalts and dacites (Serra Geral Fm.) of the Paraná Basin, after the break-up of the Gondwana Supercontinent and the opening of the South Atlantic Ocean. The 1000 m scarp has a large number of V shaped valleys and small basins to collect the debris flowing downstream. The scarp is made up by a series of steps developed by geomorphological evolution of the volcanic flows (Figure 3). The soils resulting from denudation accumulate as colluvionar prisms over the platforms. The soils are mainly composed by clays, and some of them show latteritic features.

The upper part of the debris flow structures in the Aparados da Serra region are located in the higher scarp, or in the well exposed steps of the volcanic flow in the middle scarp. The high hydraulic gradients in the upper scarp and the low hydraulic conductivity for the soils enable runoff water flow during intense rainstorms. The water flowing in the groundsurface produces cascades at scarp steps, giving rise to slope steepening by erosion of colluvionar soils. The runoff water flow and slope steepening by erosion are the main mechanisms that triggers debris flows in the Aparados da Serra region during intense rainstorms. These processes can originate small, shallow landslides; it is believed that, after initial mobilization, a complex sequence of processes take place [6]. Finally, it is important to note that upper part of the debris flow scars in the Aparados da Serra region do not show clear elliptical-shaped failure surface.

4 Debris flow modelling through GIS

The GIS modelling was performed to define "where debris flows initiate and where they can deposit". According the geologic-geomorphologic model described above, the attempt was to determine the water and sediments flow distribution, in order to predict erosion and deposition patterns in the Aparados da Serra region. The modelling algorithm was based in the Unit Stream Power – based Erosion Deposition (USPED, Mitasova and Mitas [4]). Taking into account the 2D form, the erosion/deposition prediction model was calculated through

$$ED = \nabla \, (T \cdot \mathbf{s}) = \partial(T^*\cos a)/\partial x + \partial(T^*\sin a)/\partial y \tag{1}$$

where s is the unit vector in the steepest slope direction and a is the terrain aspect. The model assume that sediment flow can be estimated by sediment transport capacity (T) as

$$T = R \, K \, C \, P \, A^m \, (\sin b)^n \tag{2}$$

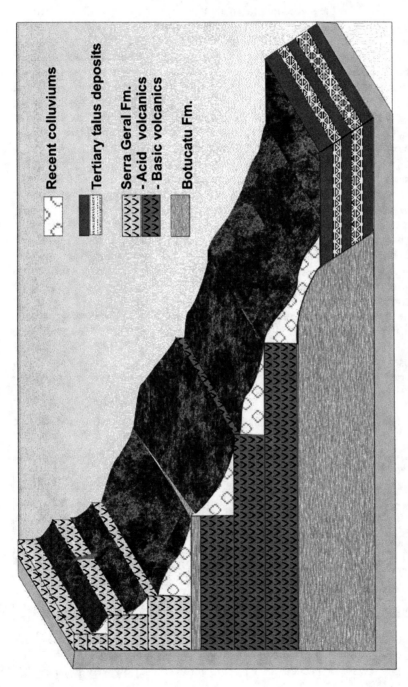

Figure 3:   Geologic-geomorphologic model for debris flow triggering in the Aparados da Serra region (Southern Brazil).

Recent colluviums

Tertiary talus deposits

Serra Geral Fm.
- Acid volcanics
- Basic volcanics

Botucatu Fm.

WIT Transactions on Engineering Sciences, Vol 60, © 2008 WIT Press
www.witpress.com, ISSN 1743-3533 (on-line)

where R is the rainfall and runoff erosivity index due to mean annual precipitation, K is the soil erodibility parameter related to physical and chemical properties of soils, C and P are parameters related to vegetation cover and management and soil uses and conservation practices, A is the slope area considered into calculation, b is solpe, m and n are constants related to runoff water and to soil types.

R parameter is calculated by the sum of erosion index (EI) values over a year divided by 100. The erosion index (EI) is a product of the kinetic energy of the falling raindrops and its maximum 30-minute period intensity. R parameter for Aparados da Serra region was calculated for a 26 years period of daily records. The mean R parameter for Aparados da Serra region is 680.

Soil erodibility parameter (K) measures the susceptibility of a given soil to erosion by rainfall and runoff. This parameter was modified to express soil types and geology (geotechnical map). Each geotechnical unit shows different amount of sand, silt, clay and organic matter, which were used to compute their *GEO* parameter (Table 1).

C parameter results from Atlantic forest cover mapping in the Aparados da Serra region, and from LANDSAT image classification procedures that distinguished between urban areas, cultivations, forest, forest plantations, grass fields, scarps, poorly vegetated areas, clouds, de-forested areas, and landslides. The computed C parameters are shown in table 2.

The soil uses and conservation practices parameter (P) is used to account for the positive impacts of such agricultural management practices. However, there exist a number of conditions related to P parameter definition. Then, for the purposes of this project, P parameter value was defined as 1, according criteria discussed by Renard et al. [7]. This value for P parameter is commonly used for steep terrains.

Table 1: *GEO* parameter computed for each geotechnical unit in the Aparados da Serra region (Southern Brazil).

Geotechnical unit	Sand	Silt	Clay	Organic matter	GEO parameter
Unit 1	7.7	54.2	34.8	3.2	0,317
Unit 2	19,2	48,1	28,9	3,8	0,325
Unit 3a	7,5	23,3	63,4	5,8	0,272
Unit 3b	22,5	38,5	35,3	3,7	0,301
Unit 4a	89,2	5	5	0,8	0,176
Unit 4b	31,4	27,6	36,2	4,8	0,291
Irati Fm.	5,9	49,8	42	2,4	0,283
Estrada Nova Fm.	2	42,2	54	1,9	0,248

The geologic-geomorphologic model discussed above accepts runoff water turbulences to promote rill and gully erosions as triggering mechanism to debris flow. In this way, the m and n are constants for overland flow were set to $m=1.6$, and $n=1.3$ [8].

Table 2:   *C* parameter computed for different vegetation cover in the Aparados da Serra region.

Classes	*C* parameter
Cities (urban areas)	0,500
Cultivations	0,600
Forest from 170 to 390 m high	0,083
Forest from 390 to 650 m high	0,085
Forest from 650 to 1010 m high	0,086
Forest from 1010 to 1135 m high	0,088
Forest from 1135 to 1200 m high	0,087
Forest plantations	0,150
Grass fields	0,100
Scarps	0,450
Poorly vegetated areas	0,450
Clouds	0.000
De-forested areas	0,450
Landslides and debris flow scars	0.600

5   Debris flow susceptibility map in Aparados da Serra region (Brazil)

The modelling was performed in ArcGIS software (ESRI), including Spatial Analyst routines. The modelling procedures were based in Mitasova et al. [9]. The coordinate system is referred to SAD69/96. The data for modelling were input in GeoUSPED file and included the DTM, the *R*, *GEO*, *C* and *P* parameters maps.

The DTM were developed using ASTER image through AsterDTM routine included in ENVI software. The spatial resolution was set in 15 m, and altitudes vary from 0 to 1430 m high.

The modelling result was divided into 4 classes: *i)* areas susceptible to erosion, *ii)* areas susceptible to deposition, *iii)* areas that show pattern interference (erosion/deposition), and *iv)* stable areas. The classified map was exported to ENVI software in order to improve the spatial consistency of the results through grouping analysis tools. A 5x5 filter was used to group similar data. The debris flow susceptibility map (Figure 4) distinguishes the erosion from deposition areas.

6   Discussion

The GIS modelling using modified USPED procedure could distinguish areas susceptible for erosion and for deposition of the debris in steep scarps, such as Aparados da Serra (Southern Brazil). This result is mainly due to the physical parameters included in GIS modelling: slope, terrain aspect, rain intensity, hydraulic gradients, vegetation cover, geologic-geotechnical conditions. All of

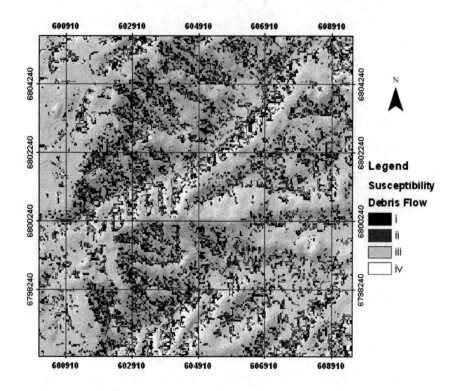

Figure 4:   Debris flow susceptibility map for Aparados da Serra region
             (Southern Brazil). Classes: I – erosion; II – deposition; III –
             transitional: erosion/deposition; IV – stable.

them are very important controlling factors for both classical erosion processes
and debris flow processes. It is to be remembered that a complex cascade of
processes can trigger debris flow [6], and such a condition is envisaged for
Aparados da Serra region.

This result (Figure 4) was compared with the large debris flow event that took
place in December 1995 (Figure 2), and also recent small scale and localized
debris flow events that are still under evaluation. All these observed debris flows
show good correlation with predicted area of occurrence. Thus, it can be
concluded that such GIS modelling can be applied to predict areas "where"
erosion and deposition of debris can take place during concentrated convective
rainstorms. The investigations are to be developed to answer "when" debris flow
can occur and "how big" the debris flow can be.

Acknowledgements

The authors want to thanks FINEP, PETROBRAS and TBG (Proc. No. 0682/01)
for research funds that supported this investigation.

References

[1] Costa, J.E., Rheologic, geomorphic, and sedimentologic differentiation of water floods, hyperconcentrated flows, and debris flows. *Flood Geomorphology*, ed. V.R. Baker, R.C. Kochel, and P.C. Patten, John Wiley and Sons, New York, p. 113–122, 1988

[2] Iverson, R.M., Schilling, S.P. & Vallance, J.W., Objective delineation of lahar-inundation hazard zones. *GSA Bulletin*, 110(8), pp. 972–984, 1998

[3] Morton, D.M., Alvarez, R.M. & Campbell, R.H., Preliminary Soil-Slip Susceptibility Maps, Southwestern California, *U.S.G.S. Open-File Report OF 03-17*, 14 pp., 2003

[4] Mitasova, H. & Mitas, L., Distributed soil erosion simulation for effective erosion prevention. Water Resources Research 34(3), pp. 505-516, 1998. Erosion/Deposition modeling with USPED tutorial, skagit.meas.ncsu. edu/~helena/gmslab/erosion/usped.html

[5] Pellerin, J., Duarte, G.M., Scheibe, L.F., Mendonça, M., Buss, M.D. & Monteiro, M.A., Timbé do Sul – Jacinto Machado: avaliação preliminar da extensão da catástrofe de 23-24/dec/1995. GEOSUL, Florianópolis (Brazil), 12(23), pp.71–86, 1997.

[6] Iverson, R.M., The physics of debris flows. American Geophysical Union, Reviews of Geophysics, 35(3), pp.245–296, 1997.

[7] Renard, K.G., Foster, G.R., Weesies, G.A., McCool, D.K. & Yoder, D.C., Predicting spoil erosion by water: a guide to conservation planning with the revised universal soil loss equation (RUSLE). Agriculture Research Service. Agriculture Handbook Number 703, 384 pp., 1996

[8] Foster, G.R., Process-based modelling of soil erosion by water on agricultural land. *Soil Erosion on Agricultural Land*, edited by J. Boardman, I.D.L. Foster & J.A. Dearing, John Wiley & Sons Ltd, pp. 429–445, 1990

[9] Mitasova, H., Brown, W.M., Hohmann, M. & Warren, S., Using soil erosion modeling for improved conservation planning: a GIS-based tutorial. Geographic Modeling Systems Laboratory, University of Illinois, http:// skagit.meas.ncsu.edu/~helena/gmslab/reports/CerlErosionTutorial, 2002

Experimental research on a grid device for the kinetic energy charge dissipation of mud-flows

G. De Martino, F. De Paola, G. Marini & A. Ranucci
Department of Hydraulic, Geotechnical and Environmental Engineering, University of Naples Federico II, Italy

Abstract

A particular grid device for kinetic energy dissipation of a mud-flow is proposed, which is already usefully employed for stilling work to service dam drainages. In this paper, the results of experimental research on a prototype realized in the Laboratory of the Department of Hydraulic and Environmental Engineering G. Ippolito are presented, with the aim of also investigating the employment of the aforesaid grid device for the dissipation of the kinetic charge of a fast mud-flow, which is a natural extreme event. The experimental installation consists of a steel pond, equipped with a particular pump group made for the purpose, and is able to raise mud-flows up to 30 l/s up to a maximum height of approximately 12 m and the aforesaid flows, by means of a slide, are directed to the device. The fast mud-flow has been reproduced by means of a mixture of water and carbonate, which is insoluble in water, characterized from a d_{50} equal to 0.0013 mm. During the tests different values of volume concentration have been adopted of between 50% and 70%, and it has been possible to control the mixture by means of continuous measures of specific weight and viscosity. The results have shown the effectiveness of the device in the presence of flows characterized with elevated Froude numbers in particular, and a beneficial effect has been induced from an obstruction wall positioned on the extremity of the grid and also by varying the full bend behind the wall (and so the empty–full ratio of the device is between 0.20–0.30), evidencing rollers that increase the total dissipative capacity of the device, which has turned out to be equal to approximately 85% in terms of kinetic charge.
Keywords: hydro-geological risk, energy dissipator, mud-flows, structural measures.

WIT Transactions on Engineering Sciences, Vol 60, © 2008 WIT Press
www.witpress.com, ISSN 1743-3533 (on-line)
doi:10.2495/DEB080111

1 Introduction

The calamitous events consequent to landslides, fast mud-flows or floods, even if it is possible to consider them as extreme natural events, have assumed a frequency for which the necessity of a structural, and not just structural measures for the mitigation of the hydro geological risk, is presented.

As far as, in particular, the structural measures for the defense from fast mud-flows are concerned, the relative works introduce many more complex problems than those classic hydraulic systems (as an example the city water-drainage system) through the lack of consolidated planning criteria [2]:
- for the non-classical aspects of such measures;
- for the complexity involved to simulate these extreme phenomena with physical or mathematical models;
- for the different modalities of beginning;
- for the limited actual knowledge of the fast mud-flow mechanics.

Moreover, while for the classical hydraulic works it is possible to define a design event with a prefixed return period, for the mud-flows is not possible to define such an event because this does not depend exclusively on the hydrological sizes.

The structural measures can be subdivided into active and passive: the first, assigned to the prevention of the mobilization phenomena of the mass, that is to the reduction of the entity of the soil volumes moved and transported down-river. The second, faced to assure the protection of the risk mud-flows areas, as well as the build-up storage of the mud and expansion areas located immediately before the inhabited zones and such to assure the disconnection between these and the depositors from which the mud-flows could be originated.

In the present work the employment of a particular grid device for the kinetic charge dissipation of fast mud-flows characterized from elevated kinetic degrees is proposed, eventually for use as an anti mud-flow structure to build-up mud storage, while estimating the effectiveness by means of experimental research still in progress.

2 Bottom grid dissipator

The grid bottom dissipators are born essentially as a disposal means to clear water. These, if well designed, offer a considerable dissipation of the kinetic charge of a flow with very elevated energy, as an example, where there is an escape from the weir flood of an artificial lake. The operation principle is based on the fact that these measures impose a double direction change to the flow by means of the same flows through a pierced slab constituting the grid.

The principal element that constitutes these structures is a channel (generally with a horizontal slope, or just a little inclined in the adverse flow direction), on whose bottom is situated a series of holes in number and sufficient dimensions in order to dispose of the coming flow from upstream: the flow passes on the grid, it crosses it changing the direction and threading in the holes, and continues towards the downstream, changing to a new direction and, by now, with a reduced kinetic charge.

The hydraulic operation of the device was studied from Prof. Carlo Viparelli [8, 9] which first showed that in relation to the conditions of upstream flow before the grid, and to the geometric characteristics of the dissipator: width, length, slope, number and dimension of the holes, empty-full ratio, various conditions of operation can take place: in slow flow, in fast flow or a flow with localized jump.

The Author supplied moreover some designing norms for the device. In particular, in the case of operation in fast flow, on the base of the following hypotheses: kinetic degree of flow Fr constant and rectilinear profile of the flow along the grid, the length L can be equal to

$$L_{Viparelli} = \frac{Q}{\frac{2}{3} b \omega \sqrt{2 g h_0} \, \mu} \qquad \text{with:} \quad \begin{array}{l} Q \text{: upstream discharge;} \\ b \text{: grid width;} \\ \omega \text{: empty-full ratio;} \\ h_0 \text{: water depth upstream grid;} \\ \mu \text{: outflow coefficient.} \end{array} \qquad (1)$$

in which the out-flow coefficient μ, function of Fr, can be calculated with the obtained formula $\mu(Fr) = 0.60 e^{-0.13Fr}$ as a result of successive tests experience [3], and in which the height of the sides of the channel that receives the grid can be established in function of the flow profile that is established along the grid.

The grid length can eventually be reduced blocking the final section of the grid [8]; such expedient, as it will become later cleared, supports the formation of macro turbulences.

The effectiveness and the efficiency of the aforesaid grid device to the aim of the reduction of the kinetic charge of clear water flows, have been subsequently verified experimentally on more models in reduced scale of works to service artificial lake drainages prepared in the Laboratory of the Department from Viparelli [8, 9] before and then from De Martino et al. [3]. This last one, in particular, leads an experimental research on a physical model in scale 1:30 of the device of dissipation to service the surface weir drainage of the Cesima tank of the surge system of Presenzano.

Sizing problems induced to reduce the length of the grid to a quarter of a that calculated with the Viparelli theory, being arranged as an obstruction wall downstream; the empty-full ratio was fixed to approximately 0.30 and the dimensions of the holes were established also taking into account the eventual necessity to leave space for larger debris carried by the flow.

Therefore the grid, of rectangular shape in the model, was 72 cm long (equal therefore in scale 1:30 to $L=L_{Viparelli}/4$) and 30 cm wide, with ten lines of six holes of rectangular section (4.33x2.33 cm) and an obstruction wall downstream.

The tests concluded that the grid dissipator can be used with good results. In particular: for the rectangular shape holes which were the most effective opportune values of the empty-full ratio comprising of between 0.25 and 0.30; the length of the grid can be much more limiting regarding that one deductible from the Viparelli theory blocking, like that suggested from the same Author, the down extremity with a wall able to favor the formation of macro turbulences that increase the dissipative effectiveness.

From the idea to use an analogous dissipator for the dissipation of the kinetic charge of a mud-flows it is part of the successive research, still in progress, first results of which were illustrated into a previous work [4], and that is, in part, the object of the present job, to estimate the eventual effectiveness in terms of energetic dissipation also in the case of fast mud-flows.

3 Experimental installation: bottom grid with obstruction wall

Using the grid of the physical model of Cesima dissipator, previously described, an experimental prototype was prepared to simulate the phenomenon of mud-flows and the eventual dissipation of energy.

The experimental installation (Fig. 1) is made up of a steel basin, of approximately 1000 l, with a particular pumping group that is able to raise a mud-flow of up to 30 l/s to a maximum height of approximately 12 m.

The basin is equipped with a recirculating system that guarantees an adapted homogeneity to the water and solid part mixture.

A flexible PVC pipe (lousiana) of 120 mm diameter, that feeds a rectangular channel with a width of 30 cm and sides of 15 cm height such to contain the maximums levels that the flow can reach on the grid, exits from the basin. The channel initially has a slope of 40%, shaping itself like a slide with a grid at its lower part, realized in Plexiglas (Fig. 2) and arranged with horizontal slope. To the end part of the grid is placed an obstruction wall with a cover that avoids the spillage of the mud and favours also the formation of macroturbulences which further help clear the flow. Under the grid there is a channel that collects the mud and takes it inside the basin, allowing the recycle.

Figure 1:   Experimental installation.

For the measurement of the flow speed and the consequent esteem of the dissipative effect of the device, there has been arranged two groups of three pitot tubes in each one. The first group is placed after the slide, immediately up-stream of the grid, and the second one immediately down-stream, in the channel of the collected mud (Fig. 2).

Figure 2:   View of the grid, up-stream and down-stream groups of Pitot tubes.

A hydraulic system is planned for measuring the muddy current kinetic load (connecting each pitot tube with the relative hydrometer) and for, when necessary, washing the small tubes (connecting each pitot tube with the washing circuit). Finally, in the section up-stream of the grid, in correspondence of the central pitot tube, a hydrometer has been placed for estimating the level (and, therefore, the flow) of the incoming muddy current.

To create the muddy mixture calcium carbonate (CALCITEC M/1) has been used, characterized by the grain curve of Fig. 3.

Calcium carbonate has been used because it is practically insoluble in water, generating a homogenous mixture and leaving at the bottom, while the pump is operating, only a small percentage of easily removable residue.

The choice of the characteristics of the mixture has been carried out taking into account studies on physical models of works that have been realized for the mitigation of hydro-geologic risk in the zones of the Campania hit from the alluvium of 5-6 May 1998 [5]. The characterization of the river bed material in such studies has allowed the characteristics for the mud used for this experimentation to be established: with the specific weight of material 430 kg/m^3, pressed specific weight 600 kg/m^3 and d_{50} equal to 0.0013 mm (Fig. 3). The chosen values can be representative of a real mud that attended the dimensions of the prototype and could be defined on the following studies of the scale problems that will be the object of further papers.

WIT Transactions on Engineering Sciences, Vol 60, © 2008 WIT Press
www.witpress.com, ISSN 1743-3533 (on-line)

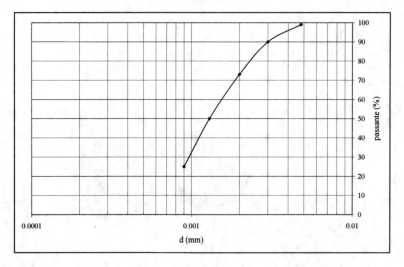

Figure 3:   Grain curve of the utilized material (CALCITEC M/1).

In the course of the tests, variable values of volume concentration have been adopted of between 50% and 70%, and it has been provided to characterize the mixture by continuous measures of specific weight and viscosity.

4 Results analysis

The experimental tests have been executed maintaining the approximately constant reologic characteristics of the mixture by subjecting it to a continuous monitoring through viscosity, concentration (in weight) and specific weight measures. For viscosity and specific weight measures, a rotational viscometer type Brooksfield and a precision balance has been used, respectively,

For the valuation of the effectiveness, reference to the percentage speed dissipation has been made, calculated referring to medium values by using the ratio between the difference of up-stream and down-stream speed and the up-stream one $(1 - V_{downstream}/V_{upstream})$.

About the reologic characteristics of the mixture, the dynamic viscosity has been maintained in the field between the values of 0,18 Pa·s and Pa·s, that corresponds to a concentration in weight between 32% and 34%. The specific weight is approximately equal to 1240 kg/m³. Within the tests carried out, the Reynolds number is always lower than 500 (the motion can be considered laminar) and the Froude number is included between 7 and 15.

The first tests have been carried out on the prototype in the configuration given in the previous paragraph, that is with a grid made up of 10 rows each with 6 holes, a length $L = L_{Viparelli}/4 = 72$ cm and an empty-full ratio $\omega = 0.30$. The obtained results are shown in Fig. 6 that displays the speed percentage dissipation on the muddy current kinetic degree incoming the grid, expressed through the Froude number ($Fr = V_{upstream}/\sqrt{gh_{upstream}}$).

They evidence that the dissipative capability of the device grows in a non-linear way to the increasing medium kinetic charge of the up-stream muddy flow and that the dissipation substantially depends on two phenomena: the first linked to the grid-effect that imposes to the current a double change of direction and the second, instead, to the impact of the same flow on the obstruction wall that involves a conspicuous loss of energy. In particular, it can be seen from the tests that for lower kinetic degree values (Fr=7÷10) of incoming muddy flow to the device, the energy dissipation is due mainly to the grid-effect since the current reaches the end of this one with a reduced energy so that it does either not hit, or only softly hits the obstruction wall; for greater values of kinetic degree (Fr=10÷15), instead, the flow hits the wall at the end of the grid. In such cases, therefore, the grid-effect is summed to the wall-effect, obtaining a meaningfully higher total dissipation catching up the maximum values of 65% in terms of speed.

Subsequent tests have been carried out in order to estimate influence on device effectiveness and efficiency of the two main planning parameters of the grid: the length (L) and the empty/full ratio (ω).

In order to know the influence of the grid length it has been reduced, leaving constant the empty/full ratio. In particular, configurations (2) and (3) have been examined. They have the following characteristic:

- (2): grid made up of 8 rows each with 6 holes ($\omega_{(2)}$=0.30, $L_{(2)}$ = 0.8L);
- (3): grid made up of 6 rows each with 6 holes ($\omega_{(3)}$=0.30, $L_{(3)}$ = 0.6L).

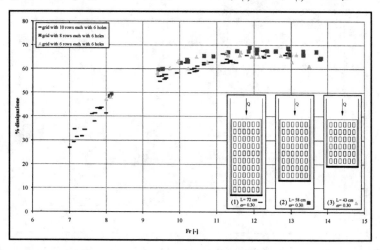

Figure 4:   Dissipative capability of the device in function of current average speed.

In Fig. 4, the results for configurations (2) and (3) and the previous one (1) are shown.

By tests carried out, it can be deduced that a further length reduction does not involve a substantial dissipative increment but only a substantial elevation of water levels with eventual risks for the sidewalls overtopping.

Therefore, a further total length reduction does not appear from the tests executed which is advisable because it would be necessary to elevate the sides in order to avoid the overtopping.

From experimental observation of the dissipative phenomenon, in correspondence of the wall, the beneficial effect of a full band at the end of the grid, next to the obstruction wall, was guessed. This solution can, in fact, favour formation of macro-turbulences that increase the total dissipative ability.

Following tests, therefore, have been finalized to the analysis of the full band influence, with ω, on the dissipation efficiency. At the beginning the grid has been modified to obtain three new configurations analogous to previous ones ((1), (2), (3)) but with the presence of an approximately 9.4 cm full bend at the end of the grid. Leaving length constant and reducing the number of holes, there's a reduction of the empty-full ratio; so the analyzed configurations are:

- (1a): grid made up of 9 rows each with 6 holes, with terminal short full bend ($\omega_{(1a)}$=0.27, $L_{(1a)}$=L, $l_{(1a)}$=0.13$L_{(1a)}$);
- (2a): grid made up of 7 rows each with 6 holes, with terminal short full bend ($\omega_{(2a)}$=0.26, $L_{(2a)}$=0.8L, $l_{(2a)}$=0.16$L_{(2a)}$);
- (3a): grid made up of 5 rows each with 6 holes, with terminal short full bend ($\omega_{(3a)}$=0.24, $L_{(3a)}$=0.6L, $l_{(3a)}$=0.22$L_{(3a)}$).

Results are shown in Fig. 5. It can be seen that there is a clean superimposition among the three configurations curves.

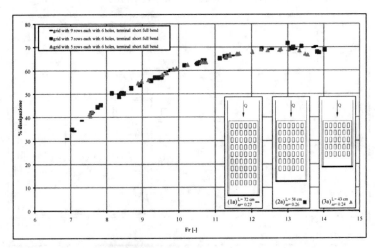

Figure 5: Dissipative capability of the device in function of current average speed (configurations with short full band).

From the results of the configurations (1), (2), (3) and (1a), (2a), (3a) it can be seen that:
- dissipation at configuration (1) is low in the examined kinetic degree field of a quantity on average of 3% in comparison with all the others;
- all values relative to all configurations, with the exception of the (1), substantially are overlapped until Fr=12;

- beyond this value, the distributions (1a), (2a) and (3a) remain however overlapped but are higher than the others, (2) and (3), of a quantity on average of 3%.

From these realizations it can be deduced that:
- in configuration (1) the dissipation is substantially entrusted to the grid effect that guarantees a maximum percentage dissipation of approximately 65%;
- in configurations (2) and (3) the wall effect takes part too; it improves the dissipative ability of device until to maximum value of approximately 67%;
- in the configurations (1a), (2a) and (3a) the maximum dissipation reach the 70% approximately, thanks to another dissipative phenomenon that is due to formation of horizontal axis vortices, as before guessed.

In fact the presence of the full band at the end of the grid, the obstruction wall next to its and the upper cover, favours the formation of macro turbulence processes (horizontal axis vortices or rollers) (Fig. 6); such vortices are settled in proximity of the obstruction wall and, absorbing a more or less conspicuous share of the kinetic energy, determine an elevated loss of total energy.

In conclusion it can be asserted that the presence of a full band, on the whole, induces an improving effect of efficiency on which the reduction of the total length of the grid is not influential, except for the increment of water levels.

Figure 6:   View of a roller.

Subsequently the length of full bend has been increased carrying it to approximately 17 cm; such operation has analogous before involved a reduction of ω. The analyzed configurations, therefore, are:
- (1b): grid with 8 rows of 6 holes with long full bend of downstream ($\omega_{(1b)}=0.24$, $L_{(1b)}=L$, $l_{(1b)}=0.23L_{(1b)}$);
- (2b): grid with 6 rows of 6 holes with long full bend of downstream ($\omega_{(2b)}=0.22$, $L_{(2b)}=0.8L$, $l_{(2b)}=0.28L_{(2b)}$);
- (3b): grid with 4 rows of 6 holes with long full bend of downstream ($\omega_{(3b)}=0.19$, $L_{(3b)}=0.6L$, $l_{(3b)}=0.38L_{(3b)}$).

The tests results are brought back in Fig. 7 from which it is possible to deduce a clean overlap between the values of the three configurations under investigation. The ulterior increase of l (and consequent reduction of ω, in this case, do not influence in an important way on the device efficiency. In fact, overlapping the results with those of the configurations (a), overlap not exemplified for space reason, finds a light increment of the dissipative capacity to the order of 2%.

If relatively to the dissipative capacity the configurations (1b), (2b) and (3b) have the same behavior, that does not happen relatively to the motion conditions that the muddy current assumes along the grid. In fact, the tests have been able to show that the hydraulic behavior of the current in the configuration (1b) is analogous to that one of the configurations (a), with short full bend, so the three effects co-exist: grid, wall and rollers. In the configurations (2b) and (3b), instead, the conditions of motion in the channel that receives the grid change and the current passes from fast to slow with the consequent formation of a hydraulic jump. In this case the great part of the dissipation must be attributed to the formation of the jump that gives to the current a large part of the energy.

Such operation must be avoided for two reasons:
- the slow current that is downstream of that jump assumes water levels much more elevated than those connecting to the fast current where, instead, there would be a jump absence and regarding which, the height of the sides of the channel that receives the grid has been calculated;
- the formation of the jump induces some depressions on the surface of the grid such to eventually being able to offend the integrity of the structure.

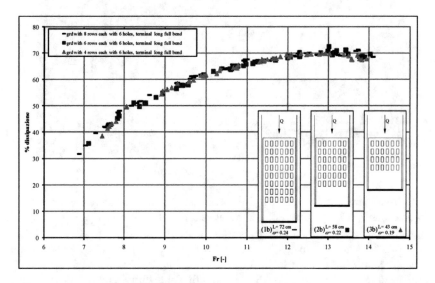

Figure 7:   Dissipative capability of the device in function of current average speed (long full band).

It can be concluded that, at least for the experiences carried out, the configuration that guarantees the better operation (fast current) and at the same time the greater dissipation percentage (maximum dissipation 72%) is (1b) characterized by length L, and $l=0.23L$.

Later on it has been verified that the eventual influence of the longitudinal slope of the grid placed leaning in the direction of the mud-flow motion. Relative to the grid that has given the best results in a horizontal position, constituted by 8 rows of 6 holes with long full downstream bend (1b), the slope is assigned by 10% and subsequently of 20%. A small improvement to the dissipation is reached in the order of 5%, 8% and is indistinct between the position at 10% and 20% of slope.

Given the small improvement in terms of dissipation, the positioning in the slope of the grid would be justifiable, in the real case, only when orography of the places allowed assigning a slope to the dispositive without excessive constructive burden.

5 Preliminary design criteria

For a preliminary sizing of a grid dissipator for mud-flows with an obstruction wall, the design flow, the known water level to the entrance of the grid, it is possible to proceed as follows:
- the Viparelli theory is applied and therefore, with the (1), the grid length $L_{Viparelli}$ is estimated fixing an empty/full ratio equal to approximately 0.25 (in the tests 0.24);
- arranging the obstruction wall to the term of the grid, the obtained length is reduced until ¼ and therefore the effective grid length becomes equal to $L=L_{Viparelli}/4$;
- the terminal grid part is computed as full bend equal to approximately 25% of L (in the tests 23%).

Lastly, if the morfologic conditions of the places allow the in slope positioning of the grid, it can also be convenient to assign some slope to the device obtaining a small improvement in dissipation.

6 Final considerations

In the present paper the results of an experimental test on a grid dissipator with obstruction wall was finalized to investigate the efficiency of them in terms of the mud-flow kinetic charge dissipation. The tests, carried out near the Laboratory of Department of Hydraulic and Environmental Engineering "G. Ippolito" of Naples, have regarded the behavior of the dissipator by varying the grid length, the downstream full bend dimension and varying the upstream current speed. The preparation of the prototype, used for the tests, has been based on the indications that have been obtained by previous theoretical studies on reduced scale models of constructions then realized for the clear water operation.

The experimental results about muddy current are satisfactory because they evidence, equal to clear water case, a good dissipative efficiency that can give a maximum of approximately 75% in terms of speed dissipation or, analogous, to 85% in terms of kinetic charge dissipation.

Three fundamental effects that characterize the dissipation phenomena have been pointed out: the grid effect that imposes to the current a double direction change, the wall effect which had an impact of the current on the obstruction final wall and the effect which had to the rollers formation. The grid effect is preponderant on the others for configurations with grid length greater or, analogous, for modest upstream current speed; the wall effect manifests itself for reduced grid length or, analogous, growing of the speed; the rollers creation, at last, is due to two concomitant conditions: the presence of full bend (that involves a ω reduction) and that one of the obstruction wall with annexed cover wall. It has been observed moreover that when the full bend length becomes a substantial share (> 30%) of the total grid length, the current passes from fast to slow with consequent creation of a hydraulic jump. Such conditions should be minimized to avoid overtopping.

References

[1] Armanini A., Darlì C., Della Putta F., Larcher M., Sartori F., (2004). "Opere diffuse per la difesa dalle colate di fango". Atti del 29° Convegno Nazionale di Idraulica e Costruzioni Idrauliche, Trento.
[2] De Martino G., Gisonni C., Giugni M., (2002). "Tipologie di interventi per la mitigazione dal rischio idrogeologico". Atti della Giornata di Studio in onore di Lucio Taglialatela, Napoli.
[3] De Martino G., Giugni M., Pulci Doria G., (1994). "Su un particolare tipo di dissipatore a griglia: primi risultati sperimentali". XXIV Convegno di Idraulica e Costruzioni Idrauliche, Napoli.
[4] De Martino G., De Paola F., Fontana N., Giugni M., (2005), "Analisi sperimentale del comportamento di un dispositivo a griglia per la dissipazione del carico energetico di una colata di fango" in Atti Convegno Nazionale La mitigazione del rischio da colate di fango a Sarno e negli altri Comuni colpiti dagli eventi del maggio 1998, Napoli, 2 e 3 Maggio 2005 - Sarno 4 e 5 Maggio 2005
[5] CUDAM, Verifica su modello fisico in scala ridotta delle opere per il rimodellamento del versante tra il vallone Connola e il vallone S. Francesco in località Quindici – Relazione Finale, 2002
[6] Mizuyama T., Yazawa A., (1987), "A computer simulation for debris flow processes", Erosion and sedimentation in Pacific Rim, Proceedings of the Corvallis Symposium, IAHS pubbl. N. 165.
[7] Versace P., (2001). "La riduzione del rischio idrogeologico nei comuni colpiti dagli eventi del maggio '98 in Campania". Atti del Forum per il Rischio Idrogeologico in Campania – Fenomeni di colata rapida di fango nel maggio '98, Commissariato di Governo per l'Emergenza Idrogeologica in Campania, Napoli.
[8] Viparelli C., (1961). "Dissipatori a griglia di fondo". Pubblicazione n. 148 dell'Istituto di Idraulica e Costruzioni Idrauliche dell'Università di Napoli.
[9] Viparelli C., (1963). "Dissipatori a griglia di fondo". L'Energia Elettrica, 7.

Section 3
Case studies

Evaluation of debris flow hazard to Chalala village, Quebrada de Humahuaca UNESCO World Heritage Site, Jujuy Province, Argentina

M. A. González[1], V. Baumann[1] & L. E. Jackson Jr.[2]
[1]SEGEMAR, Capital Federal, Buenos Aires, Argentina
[2]Pacific Division, Geological Survey of Canada, Vancouver, BC, Canada

Abstract

Chalala village is situated on the alluvial fan of Quebrada Chalala that is periodically affected by extensive debris flows. Servicio Geológico Minero Argentino (SEGEMAR) sought to establish the magnitude and frequency of debris flows from unmonitored Chalala basin. Analysis of historical records, oral accounts, and investigations of debris flow deposits and surveys of two debris flows in 2007 assigned Chalala and adjacent Coquena fans to high frequency and large magnitude ratings in semi-quantitative hazard rating schemes. Two methods were used to estimate the volume of the maximum likely debris flow for the purposes of debris-flow-defence design and hazard evaluation. Method one extrapolated known peak discharge/total volume relationships using a power relationship for debris (mud) flows displaying similar rheology. Method 2 involved extrapolation of known extreme sediment yield values. The methods yielded comparable results for the two basins. The method 2 estimate of $4.6 \times 10^5 m^3$ is consistent with geomorphic and stratigraphic investigations and eyewitness accounts of events over the past 62 years. An additional uncertainty coefficient of 1.2 is recommended.
Keywords: debris flow, mudflow, Argentina, Andes, Humahuaca, Purmamarca.

1   Introduction

Debris flows and debris floods are widespread hazards throughout the Andes from Venezuela to Argentina [1–3]. Unlike analogous mountainous drainage basins of the European and Japanese alps and parts of the North American cordillera, most of the Andes and other mountainous areas of the developing world have sparse hydro-meteorological data collection. Under these circumstances, investigators commonly have to evaluate debris flow hazard based upon scattered written or oral accounts from local residents and deposits of historic or prehistoric debris flows. This paper describes an investigation by Servicio Geológico Minero Argentino (SEGEMER) of debris flow hazard to the recently established village of Chalala in Quebrada de Humahuaca UNESCO world heritage site, Jujuy Province, Argentina. It was carried out in conjunction with the Multinational Andean Project: Geoscience for Andean Communities (MAP:GAC), a collaborative undertaking by geological surveys of the Andean countries and Canada. We show how a mix of data sources typically available to investigators in sparsely monitored mountain regions can be combined with empirical relationships established elsewhere to evaluate debris flow hazard.

2 Physical and climatic setting

The new village of Chalala is located on the alluvial fan of Quebrada de Chalala (quebrada is 'creek' in English) a tributary to Río de la Quebrada de Purmamarca (Río Purmamarca) in the western half (Mitad Occidental) of the Cordillera Oriental of the Andes of northwestern Argentina (area of $23°43'56"$ S, $65°30'60"$ W; Fig. 1). It covers 5 Ha and consists of 50 houses. The resort town of Purmamarca is 2 km to the southwest. The terrain of Cordillera Oriental closely reflects structure and lithology of an easterly verging fold and thrust belt. Peaks rise to 4200 m and relief in the Purmamarca area is in the 2000 to 2500 m range. Secondary streams cut deep, ravine-like dendritic valley systems east and

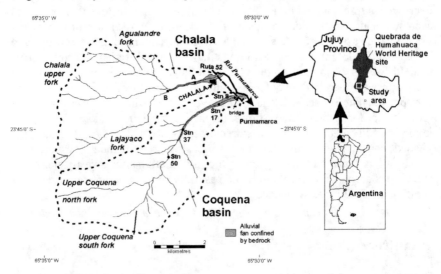

Figure 1:   Location of study area and features referred to in text.

west from major north-south valleys. Quebrada Chalala and adjacent Quebrada Coquena are typical examples of these tributaries (Table 1). The lower reaches of Quebrada Chalala and adjacent Quebrada Coquena occupy elongated sediment filled valleys laterally constrained by bedrock spurs rather than classic alluvial fans where stream courses are free to migrate laterally across an arc of 45 degrees or more. The macroclimate of the region is arid subtropical modified by elevation. Average temperature is in the 12 to 14° C range in valley locations such as Chalala. However, winter temperatures as low as −8.8° C and between 30° and 35°C throughout the year have been recorded [4]. Adjacent mountains have progressively lower maximum temperatures and increasingly rigorous physical weathering environments with altitude. Total annual rainfall is less than 200 mm and it occurs during the austral summer months of November to March. Relative humidity is usually less than 50% and evaporative potential is 2000 mm. Consequently, vegetation is sparse to absent.

Table 1:   Physiographic statistics for Chalala and Coquena basins.

Basin	Area (km^2)	Max. elev. (m asl)	Max. relief, (m)	Channel length (m) /slope above fan-head (deg.)	Fan area above Ruta 52 (m^2)	Mean fan slope
Chalala	19.6	4178	1721	6295/12-17	2.5x10^5	4.2°
Coquena	19.4	4087	1621	3785/17.5	3.8x10^5	4.0°

3   Study methods

The regional geology and geomorphology of the area was previously studied by SEGEMAR [5]. A high resolution Ikonos satellite image was taken (June 2006) in order to study the geomorphology of the basin and prepare an accurate digital elevation model and topographic map. Although this study had as its objective the evaluation of debris flow hazard the village of Chalala, information gathered on the adjacent Quebrada Coquena basin (see below) was directly applicable to the Chalala basin. Both basins and their fans were investigated.

3.1 Surveys of 7 and 30 March the debris flow deposits

Width, thickness (from natural exposures) and slope angle were measured from flow toe to fan head over segments 50 to 100 m in length. Thickness was estimated for each segment based upon natural exposures. The volume of each segment was calculated. Volumes were considered maximum estimates and could be up to about 30% larger than true values due to lack of exposures in estimating flow thickness. Where bends in the flow path were sharp enough to cause super-elevation of a flow on the outside of the bend relative to the inside of the bend, flow velocity (v) was estimated using a the force-vortex equation (1) of Hungr [6]. Where run-up against barriers occurred, velocity was estimated using the equation (2) of Chow [7].

$$v = ((\Delta h \; r \; g \; j)/ b)^{0.5} \tag{1}$$
$$v = (2 \; g \; \Delta h)^{0.5} \tag{2}$$

WIT Transactions on Engineering Sciences, Vol 60, © 2008 WIT Press
www.witpress.com, ISSN 1743-3533 (on-line)

where v = flow velocity, Δh = the difference in elevation between the inside and outside of the channel (1) or the relative run-up height (2); g = acceleration of gravity 9.8 m/s/s; r = the radius of a circle approximating the curve of the channel; b = the width of the debris flow across the super-elevation; and j is a constant assumed to be 1 for these calculations (j is suggested to be 2.5 as a safety factor for design of bends in debris flow containment dikes by Hungr et al. [8]. Peak discharge was computed by multiplying channel cross sectional area immediately up-stream from the curvature in the channel where the super-elevation was measured. The super-elevated cross section cannot accurately be used as a cross section because flows have been observed to have pronounced concavities during super-elevation [9, 10].

3.2 Estimation of past debris flow magnitude from geomorphic evidence

The fans and lower basins of quebradas Coquena and Chalala were traversed in order to search for evidence and sectional exposures of debris flow deposits. In the areas of fan heads, the highest and widest debris flow levees were measured. Ages of the levees were determined by ^{14}C dating or estimated from 'silent witnesses' including ages and injuries to trees (*salix* sp.) and cardón cactus (*Echinopsis atacamensis*). The latter can grow to heights of 4 m. Their ages were estimated by assuming a vertical growth rate of 5 cm/year. These are minimum estimates because decades may elapse between levee deposition and establishment of the cactus. Also, it is not clear at what height, if any, vertical growth ceases.

3.3 Interviews of eyewitnesses and compilation of written and oral history

Witnesses of the 7 March 2007 debris flows could estimate its velocity from direct observation. Furthermore, an estimate of its average velocity traversing the length of the fan could also be computed from their accounts by dividing the fan length by their estimates of the time from the initial sound of its approach (emergence at fan head) until it passed them. Elders who lived their lives on the fans or within the basins of quedradas Coquena and Chalala documented the dates and magnitude of past debris flows. They established that debris flows were associated with intense mountain thunderstorms or regional rainstorms.

4   Debris flows in the Purmamarca area

Sparse vegetation and high relief make the Purmamarca area particularly prone to debris flows during periods of intense rain. Unfortunately, historical documentation of floods and debris flows only post-date 1945 (Table 2). Events all occurred during summer months (November to March) when almost all yearly precipitation falls. During these events, rain falls on the upper basins and may or may not fall in the Río Purmamarca valley. Rain fell on the mountains and valleys during the 1984 event. A surge of water and sediment was recorded on Río Purmamarca at a now abandoned Río Grande railway station 3 km to the east of Purmamarca. It appeared like a wall as it approached. It was likely a debris flood [11] rather than a true debris flow.

Table 2:   Historic debris flows in Purmamarca area from written and oral accounts and surveys in 2007.

Date	Chalala	Coquena	Purma-marca	Max length[a]/ width (m)	Est. total vol. (m^3)
2007 (7 Mar.)		X		4100/116	1.1×10^5- 1.5×10^5
2007 (29 Mar.)	X			2296/42	1.6×10^4
2002[b]		X		--	<2007 event
1986 (Nov. 11)	X			2296/100	Unknown
1984 (11 Feb.)			X	--	--
1970 (Dec.[b])	X			--	--
1970 (8 Feb.)			X	--	--
1960 (Feb[b])			X	--	--
1957 (late Dec.)	X			--	*volcán*[c]
1949[b]			X	--	--
1945[b]	X				

a. Lengths determined from fan head; b. day and month uncertain; c. lahar-scale mudflow.

4.1 Investigation of 7 and 29 March 2007 debris flows

Table 3 summarizes the unified soil classification and Atterberg limits for samples from 7 and 29 March debris flows. Locations of points referred to in the discussion are shown in Fig. 1. The debris flow of 7 March 2007 reached the head of the fan of Quebrada Coquena at approximately 5 AM. It followed a thunderstorm over the basin of Quebrada Coquena an hour earlier. A witness who lives within the drainage identified the north fork of Quebrada Coquena as the source of the mudflow (Fig. 1). It travelled the 4 km length of the fan in an estimated 10 to 15 minutes for an estimated average speed of 4–7 m/s. A witness at station 8 (channel gradient 3.5 degrees) about 150 m above the Ruta 52 bridge described the flow as very turbulent. He estimated the flow velocity to have been faster that he could run to save his life (at least 5 to 6 m/s for a young man is a reasonable estimate) and noted that the flow continued for about 10 minutes. The fluidity and turbulence of the flow on a very low gradient clearly indicate that it was a mudflow despite its borderline plasticity index of 4.9 (Table 5) that places it just below the mudflow classification of Hungr et al. [8] (>5%). It descended channels along the lower fan with gradients as low as 3 degrees and transported clasts up to 43 cm in maximum diameter to Río Purmamarca. Clasts up to 180 cm in maximum diameter were transported to the fan head. Approximately 2300 m^3 of stony muddy debris passed a vertical gap about 1 m high and 12.7 m in width on a gradient of 3 degrees between bridge and channel floor (Figs. 3 and 4). High pore pressures remained in the debris flow deposits as late as 13 March: sediments still spontaneously flowed in excavations near the highway bridge at that time. In many areas, the bouldery facies of the debris flow was buried by muddy after-flow facies.

Table 3:   Classification debris flow samples.

Sample	Fan	Source	USC	LL (%)	PL (%)	PI (%)
36	Chalala	Pre-2007 deposit	SC	21.9	14.5	7.4
38	Coquena	Fresh flow	SM-SC	23.7	18.8	4.9
39	Chalala	Fresh flow	GP-GM	26.3	21.5	5.2
40	Chalala	Fresh flow	no data	24.5	16.4	8.1

Table 4:   Summary of velocity and discharge data determined from a survey of 7 March, 2007 debris flow from Quebrada Coquena.

Stations	Δh (m)	b (m)	r (m)	v (m/s)	X-section area (m²)	Max Q (m³/s)
Super-elevation method (equation 1)						
50-1	3.4	14	55	7.7	62	477
50-2	3.4	14	55	7.7	40	308
50-3	4.1	14	55	8.5	62	527
50-4	4.1	14	55	8.5	40	340
17-1				4.7		
Run-up method (equation 2)						
50-5	3.4			8.2	62	508
50-6	3.4			8.2	40	328
50-7	4.1			9	62	588
50-8	4.1			9	40	360
37-1	1			4.4	-	-
17-2	1			3.6-4.6	-	-
Eyewitness and other estimates						
Average velocity along length of fan				4.6-7	-	-

Table 5:   Ages of largest prehistoric debris flows, quebradas Coquena and Chalala.

Basin/Sub-basin or fan	Age (years)	Control and other comments
Chalala/ Agualandre	>200-300	Minimum est. age of cardón cactus growing on highest levee.
Chalala/ Chalala	<670	^{14}C age 620+/-80 bp (Beta 231191) detrital wood in highest debris flow deposits.
Chalala/Lajayaco	>200-300	Minimum age estimate from estimated age of cardón cactus growing on deposit.
Chalala: deposit on fan	1957 event?	1.4 to 2 m thick debris flow deposits in bank of q. Chalala (pt. A, Fig. 1). Unvegetated except for scattered small bushes.
Coquena; station 50	>200? flows	Willow tree growing on highest levee (est. >100 <200 years) It was damaged by debris flow larger than 2007 during its life.

The 29 March debris flow reached the lower part of Quebrada Chalala in darkness at 8:30 PM. It was preceded by a storm that began with the fall of hail followed by heavy rain for about 40 minutes from 8:00 to about 8:40 PM. At the Chalala village, it filled the 20 m wide channel to an estimated depth of 2 m. The flow continued for about 10 minutes. It crossed Ruta 52 burying it to a depth of 50 cm. It continued on to Río Purmamarca and crossed the channel but did not dam it. It was clearly a mudflow. It descended gradients as low as 2.5 degrees

and had a plasticity index >5% (Table 3). Comparison of Ikonos satellite images before and after determined that the flow originated in parts of the Lajayaco and Agualandre sub-basins.

4.2 Prehistoric debris flows

Bouldery debris flow levees occur at fan heads and deposits of debris flow diamicton locally occur up to 4 m above channel floors upstream from fan heads. They are the remains of the largest magnitude debris flows. Silent witnesses or radiocarbon dating assign these deposits to periods predating written or oral records (Table 5). The three principal tributaries of Quebrada Chalala join about 2 km above the Chalala village and mark the upper limit of the linear bedrock-confined alluvial fan of Quebrada Chalala (Fig. 1). Each tributary has evidence of prehistoric debris flows that were significantly larger than historical events. Quebrada Coquena emerges from a narrow bedrock valley upstream from station 50. The canyon splits into three tributaries about 1 km above station 50 (Fig. 1).

They have narrow bedrock-walled channels. Consequently, evidence of older and larger debris flows is confined to the area around station 50. Deposits in this area have muddy matrices similar to the 2007 debris flows. They indicate that previous events were also highly mobile mudflows e.g. Table 5, sample 36.

5   Frequency and magnitude of debris flow hazard on fans of quebradas Coquena and Chalala

Although only the debris flows of the 7 and 29 March 2007 have been investigated in detail, the combined historical and prehistoric evidence from the two basins can be used to place the two fans within established semi-quantitative hazard rating schemes. The two watersheds are geologically identical. Records from one can be used to corroborate, augment, and evaluate the record of the other. Debris flows large and mobile enough to traverse the entire lengths of the two fans and reach Río Purmamarca have occurred twice in 21 years. Smaller events have also occurred on both fans during that time. That record clearly places these fans in the very high probability (<1/20) range of Hungr [6]. With respect to magnitude, the volume of the 2007 debris flow on the fan of Quebrada Coquena exceeded 10^5 m^3. The last large debris flow on the Quebrada Chalala fan in 1957 (Tables 2 and 5) was described as a *volcán*, a term reserved for an extremely large lahar-like mudflow in this region. Witnesses described it as being 4-5 m thick in the fan head (Fig. 1, B). Deposits from this event are apparently exposed at A (Fig. 1) and are at least 2 m thick at that mid fan location. Debris flows with volumes in the 10^5–10^6 m^3 range fall within Class 5 of the magnitude classification scheme of Jakob [9]. Such events are capable of destroying parts of villages such as Chalala, burying highways and blocking small rivers such as Río Purmamarca.

Although relative rating schemes employed above give a general evaluation for the debris flow hazard to Chalala village, design of debris flow defences such as protective dykes or dams and physical or computer modelling require more quantitative estimates of the largest debris flow likely to occur. Two methods were used to achieve this. They are described below.

5.1 Method 1: extrapolation of peak discharge/total discharge relationships

Power relationships between peak discharge (Q_p) and total discharge (V) of debris flows have been compiled for areas of the European and Japanese alps, North American cordillera and other mountainous regions [9,12]. These compilations have also characterized these power relationships based on debris flow texture and rheology e.g. bouldery and noncohesive debris flows versus very fluid mudflows. Reference to this literature permits application of power relationships expressed as $V = c\,Q_p^{\,n}$ (c is a dimensionless constant). A search of the literature found equation (3) of Bovis and Jakob [13] for very fluid debris flows from British Columbia, Canada to best approximate the peak to total discharge relationships seen along quebradas Coquena and Chalala.

$$V=338Q_p^{\,0.99} \tag{3}$$

The range of peak discharges calculated from data collected at station 50 (Table 4) yielded a range of predicted total discharges between 1.1×10^5 and 1.9×10^5 m^3 with a mean of 1.4×10^5 m^3. This compares well with the surveyed value of 1.5×10^5 m^3. Table 6 computes the total discharges for basin-wide debris flows for Quebrada Coquena at Station 50 and for the Lajayaco fork of Quebrada Chalala using cross sectional channel areas from field measurement of the channel defined by the highest levees. An estimate of the discharge for the entire basin is made by scaling this discharge to the other sub-basins based on their relative areas.

Table 6: Predicted total volume (V) for the prehistoric debris flows from Quebrada Coquena and Lajayco fork (Quebrada Chalala), equation (3).

Basin or sub-basin	Channel cross sectional area (m^2)	Estimated Q_p (m^3/s) assuming v=7.9 m/s	Predicted V (m^3) assuming $V=338Q_p^{\,0.99}$
q. Coquena above sta. 50	98	776	2.5×10^5
q. Chalala (Lajayaco)	63	498	1.6×10^5
Values for other Chalala tributaries scaled drainage area			
q. Chalala (middle fork)			1.3×10^5
Agualandre			0.9×10^5
Total Chalala basin			3.8×10^5

5.2 Method 2: modified JICA debris yield method

This method was used in the investigation of debris flow hazard in the arid Río Rimac basin, Peru by the Japan International Cooperation Agency (JICA) [14] and Fidel et al. [15]. Total debris flow volume is predicted for a basin using sediment yield/unit basin area based upon yield ratios determined for the largest known debris flow in the local region. This is assumed to be a low probability event. The 5.6 km^2 northern sub-basin of Quebrada Coquena (Fig. 1) was the source of the 7 March debris flow. We regarded this as a >1:20 year event.

Although the north fork upper Coquena sub-basin is 36% of the entire Quebrada Coquena basin, peak discharge from this event was in the order of 60% of that estimated for largest prehistoric debris flow based on field evidence at station 50. The sediment yield ratio for north fork Quebrada Coquena ranged between $2.7x10^4$ and $2.0x10^4$ m^3/km^2 for this event (compare to $2x10^3$ m^3/km^2 for the Lajayaco and Agualandre sub-basins, the sources of the 29 March, 2007 debris flow). Maximum and minimum estimates for total debris flow volumes based on these yield values are shown in Table 7 and are compared with the results of method 1.

Table 7:   Predicted   maximum   discharges   using   method   2   (JICA methodology).

Basin or sub-basin	Area (km^2)	V (yield ratio $2.7x10^4$ m^3/km^2)	V (yield ratio $2.0x10^4$ m^3/km^2)	V (m^3) Table 6 (Method 1)
Coquena above station 50	12.4	$3.3x$ 10^5 m^3	$2.5x10^5$ m^3	$2.5x10^5$
Chalala (all sub basins above fan head)	16.9	$4.6x10^5$ m^3	$3.4x10^5$ m^3	$3.8 x10^5$

6   Discussion

Methods 1 and 2 produced similar results for maximum debris flow volumes expected for the fans of quebradas Coquena and Chalala based upon different methods. As reassuring as this mutual corroboration appears, it must be noted that the data sets that were used by both methods were partly related. Consequently, it must be asked if there is any independent evidence to suggest that any of these estimated maximum debris flow volumes are realistic. We assert that geomorphic and stratigraphic evidence unrelated to these data sets can be used to evaluate whether or not they are realistic. With respect to method 2 (JICA method), maximum estimated debris flow volumes are based on the assumption that during the largest debris flow event, sediment is mobilized throughout the entire Chalala and Coquena basins at the yield rates determined for the source sub-basin (north fork) of the 7 March debris flow. For the Coquena basin, the highest and widest debris flow levees at station 50 define a channel with a cross sectional area of approximately 1.4 times that occupied by the 7 March debris flow. Assuming equation (3) and using a peak velocity of 8 m/s, a debris flow of $3.3x10^5$ m^3 would require a channel cross sectional area of approximately 1.3 times that of the 7 March debris flow. Thus, we conclude that the maximum specific yield value of $2.7x10^4$ m^3/km^2 is reasonable value to apply to the entire basin for the largest debris flow to have occurred in the Coquena basin during the past several hundreds of years.

With respect to the Chalala basin, a maximum debris flow volume of $4.6x10^5$ m^3 is computed if the same specific yield value is applied (it is essentially geologically and physiographically identical to Coquena basin). A flow of this size would cover the fan of Quebrada Chalala to an average depth of approximately 1.8 m. Our collection of oral accounts of debris flow events evidence indicates that the 1957 debris flow, which predates Chalala village, was apparently of this magnitude. Deposits several m thick in the area of the fan head were reported by witnesses of this event. Stratigraphic evidence corroborates such an event on Chalala fan within this time frame. An exposure at Point A (Fig.1) shows a succession of stratified debris flow diamictons. The uppermost flow is 2 m thick. The same flow was thick enough to transport a 1 m^3 quartzite block to the area of Chalala village. Judging by the lack of vegetation on this flow, it is only decades old and may date from either 1986 or the 1957 *volcán* (Table 5).

Based on this additional geomorphological evidence, we conclude that both methods 1 and 2 compute reasonable estimates for the volume of design debris flows. However, maximum values from method 2 appear to yield the most conservative estimates. This notwithstanding, the JICA method [14] applies an additional safety coefficient of 1.2 to allow for uncertainty. We suggest that it should be applied to method 2 estimates following JICA methodology.

References

[1] Carlotto, V., Fídel, L., Guzmán, A. Valenzuela, G.. and Huamaní, A., Colapso y fljo de detritos de Aobamba, Cusco, Perú, Proyecto Multinacional Andino: Geociencias para las Comunidades Andinas 2007. Movimientos en Masa en la Región Andina: Una guía para la evaluación de amenazas. Servicio Nacional de Geologia y Mineria, Publicación Geológica Multinacional, **4**, pp. 303–307, 2007.

[2] González D., E.F., González, M. A., Ramallo Diego A., E., Flujo de detritos (alluvión) del 4 del abril del 2001 de Palma Sola, Jujuy, Argentina, Proyecto Multinacional Andino: Geociencias para las Comunidades Andinas 2007. Movimientos en Masa en la Región Andina: Una guía para la evaluación de amenazas. Servicio Nacional de Geologia y Mineria, Publicación Geológica Multinacional, **4**, pp. 285–291. 2007.

[3] Salcedo, D.A. (2007) Flujo de detritos del Río Limón, al norte de Marcay, Estado Aragua, Venezuela. Proyecto Multinacional Andino: Geociencias para las Comunidades Andinas 2007. Movimientos en Masa en la Región Andina: Una guía para la evaluación de amenazas. Servicio Nacional de Geologia y Mineria, Publicación Geológica Multinacional, No. 4, pp. 269–272.

[4] Estación Experimental INTA - SALTA. Instituto Nacional de Tecnología Agropecuaria. Boletín Desideratum Jueves 31 de Julio de 2003 - Año I - N° 10. ISSN 1667-6580: http://www.inta.gov.ar/salta/info/boletines/desideratum/boletin_desideratum10.htm

[5] SEGEMAR Estudio geológico integrado de la quebrada de Humahuaca: Geología regional y geomorfología. Instituto De Geología Y Recursos Minerales. Buenos Aires, Argentina (CD-ROM), 1998.

[6] Hungr, O. Some methods of landslide hazard intensity mapping. Proceedings of a landslide risk workshop, ed. R. Fell & D.M. Cruden, A.A. Balkema., Rotterdam, pp. 215–226, 1997.

[7]   Chow, V.T., Open channel hydraulics, McGraw Hill, New York, 680 p., 1959.
[8]   Hungr, O, Evans, S.G., Bovis, M., & Hutchison, J.N. Review of the classification of landslides of the flow type. Environmental and engineering geoscience, **4**, pp. 231–228, 2001.
[9]   Jakob, M., Debris-flow hazard and analysis, Debris flow hazards and related phenomena, ed. M. Jakob and O. Hungr,. Springer-Praxis books in geophysical sciences, Chichester, pp. 411–443, 2005.
[10] Jakob, M., Personal communication, October, 2007, Principal, BGC Engineering, Vancouver, Canada.
[11] Pierson, T.C., Hyperconcentrated flow—transitional process between water flow and debris flow, Debris flow hazards and related phenomena, ed. M. Jakob and O. Hungr, Springer-Praxis books in geophysical sciences, Chichester, pp. 159–202, 2005.
[12] Rickenmann, D., Empirical relationships for debris flows, Natural hazards, **19**, pp. 47–77, 1999.
[13] Bovis, M.J. and Jakob, M., The role of debris supply conditions in predicting debris flow activity. Earth   Surface Processes and Landforms, **24**, pp. 1039–1054, 1999.
[14] Japan International Cooperation Agency (JICA). Final report for the master plan study on the disaster prevention project in the Rimac River basin. Japan International Cooperation agency, Tokyo, 6 vol., 1988.
[15] Fidel S., L., Zegarra L., J., Vilchez M., M., Franco-Castillo N., L., & Jackson, L.E., Jr., Evolution of landslide activity, and the origin of debris flows in the El Niño affected Payhua Creek basin, Matucana area, Huarochiri, Peru, Proceedings, Engineering geology for tomorrow's cities, *the 10th IAEG International Congress, Nottingham, United Kingdom*, paper **32**, 12 p., 2006.

The debris flow in Log pod Mangartom, NW Slovenia

M. Zorn & B. Komac

Anton Melik Geographical Institute, Scientific Research Centre of the Slovenian Academy of Sciences and Arts, Slovenia

Abstract

In November 2000, heavy rains in Slovenia triggered numerous slope processes. Among the largest were the landslide and debris flow in Log pod Mangartom in western Slovenia. This paper describes the main geographical, geological, and geomechanical features of the debris flow, detailing its causes and describing the consequences. The facts presented in the article demonstrate that intensive geomorphic processes are relatively frequent phenomena and are an important factor in the transformation of the surface in alpine regions.

Keywords: geography, geomorphology, natural hazards, slope processes, debris flow, landslide, Log pod Mangartom, Slovenia.

1   Introduction

Log pod Mangartom (651 m; population about 130) is a nucleate roadside settlement located on the right bank of the Koritnica River on the alluvial fan of its tributary Predelica stream. On November 17, 2000, a debris flow struck the village. According to Ogrin [11], the Koritnica Valley has a temperate continental climate. Between 1961 and 1990, an annual average of 2,500 mm of precipitation was recorded, and avalanches regularly threaten the valley floor [13]. The area is part of Triglav National Park.

2   Debris flow

At 12:45 on November 15, 2000, a landslide was triggered west of Mount Mangart (2,679 m) above the valley of the Mangartski Potok stream, which has an inclination greater than 10%. The landslide stopped almost two kilometers

WIT Transactions on Engineering Sciences, Vol 60, © 2008 WIT Press
www.witpress.com, ISSN 1743-3533 (on-line)
doi:10.2495/DEB080131

lower at the valley's junction with the Predelica Valley. Lying between the altitudes of 1,340 and 1,580 meters, the original site of the slide material was 900 meters long and three to four hundred meters wide. The average thickness of the slide in source area was ten meters, and it reached forty meters in places. In all, 1.5 million cubic meters of material was shifted [6]. Above the slide, crown cracks appeared that extended to the watershed divide ridge.

Due to the heavy rain, the streams grew greatly. For 35 hours and 20 minutes, water soaked the slide material deposited on the floor of the Mangartski Potok valley until it became liquefied on November 17, 2000. A few minutes after midnight, a debris flow was triggered that traveled almost three kilometers downwards at a speed approaching eight meters per second [17].

Figure 1:   Aerial photograph of the event. (Source: Orthophotographic image, © Geodetic Survey of Slovenia, 2005.)

2.1 Primary reasons and causes of the debris flow

The primary cause of the debris flow was heavy and intense precipitation. The rain gauge in the village of Log pod Mangartom recorded 1,638.4 mm of rainfall (more than 60% of the average annual precipitation) in the 48 days before the events. This amount of recorded rainfall has a recurrence interval of more than 100 years. The increase in runoff coefficients in the autumn of 2000 during the rainy period before the landslide was therefore two- to threefold higher than usual. Additional water was contributed by the permanent but slow seepage of underground water from a reservoir in the slope [8]. Abundant flow of water in the body of the landslide located in the Mangartski Potok valley that created a state of liquefaction [14].

An important cause of this event is the geological structure, particularly the 100- to 200-meter thick layers of Julian-Tuval limestone, marlaceous limestone, marl, and schist claystone. These so called Tamar or Rabelj (Raibl) layers alternate in the 700-meter deep stratified, tectonically damaged, and porous Karnian and Norian dolomite. At their contact are springs that are an added significant cause of landslides. The tectonically damaged rock also makes the slopes unstable [3].

The clay minerals of the Tamar layers absorb water and swell and the schist claystone decomposes into clay, which leads to sliding. The low plasticity creeping material contains 20–30% fine particles (< 63 μm) and is thixotropic. With a small increase in moistness, the viscosity and shear limit drop very rapidly and therefore the material liquefies with only small changes in its water content. Approximately 33% moisture is sufficient to cause liquefaction [7].

Table 1:   Main geotechnical parameters of the debris flow deposit [8].

Specific gravity	27–28.5 kN/m^3
Average unit weight of in situ samples	~22 kN/m^3
Average dry unit weight	18 kN/m^3
Porosity of material in situ	34%
Water content of material in situ	34%
Degree of saturation of material in situ	100%
Hydraulic conductivity	<25·10^{-6} m/s

Among the causes of the landslide, we cannot completely exclude the influences of the fissures that developed in the slopes after the "Easter earthquake" of April 12, 1998, after which water was able to flow more rapidly into the depths [10, 22]. Also, the fissures may have changed or opened new groundwater pathways through fractured dolomite layers in the slope [8]. A lack of vegetation cover also causes greater erodibility and vulnerability to landslides. The area, including the slide area, was overgrown with forest, which could have influenced the change in the water conditions. However, several decades ago the area was clearcut, and today Norway spruce (*Picea abies*) grows instead of beech (*Fagus sylvatica*). The mass of wood did not influence the stability of the slopes, however, since it only comprised 1/100,000 of the entire mass of the material in the landslide [4].

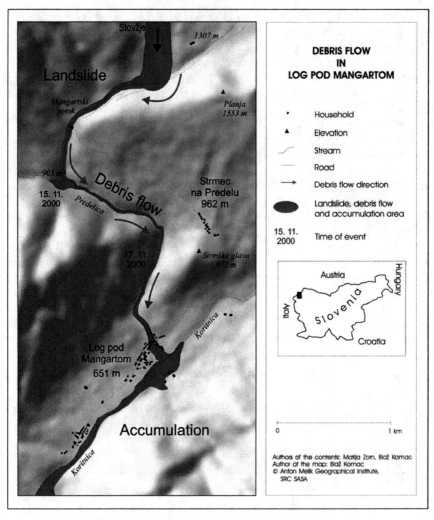

Figure 2: Map of the Log pod Mangartom landslide and debris flow.

2.2 Consequences of the debris flow

The annual sediment production in the headwaters of alpine valleys in western Slovenia is estimated to average $>1,000$ m^3 km^{-2} a^{-1}, which means that rock falls and debris flows are an important factor in the transformation of alpine regions. Large amounts of material are usually transferred to lower sites in a very short time.

After the 1998 earthquakes in the Soča Valley, about 260,000 m^3 of rock fall material was expected to remain in its original position, while an estimated volume of 480,000 m^3 could possibly be released to watercourses over a longer period during extreme events. About 200,000 m^3 of rock fall debris was deposited in areas from where the material could be released to watercourses during future rainfall events [9].

During the debris flow in 2000, a total of 1.5 million cubic meters of material moved. Part of the material was deposited in the bed of the Predelica stream, and more that a million cubic meters was deposited over an area of fifteen hectares in the Koritnica Valley (Figure 4). For almost three kilometers, the valley floor was covered with a layer of alluvium several meters thick.

The Koritnica River carried off a great deal of sediment: above its confluence with the Koritnica, the Soča River near Kršovec contained only 104 g/m^3 of suspended material while at the confluence it contained 2,971 g/m^3. On November 21, 2000, the highest concentration ever recorded in the Soča, 8,112 g/m^3, was measured [20].

Mud flows formed in the deposited sediment to form a lake that threatened the Mangartska Planina mountain lodge. Similar "clay bombs" (Figure 3) could also be found in the Koritnica Valley, where they gradually deteriorated into characteristic conical mounds [2].

Figure 3:   "Rubble-clay bomb" (Photograph: Blaž Komac, November 30, 2000).

The natural disaster in Log pod Mangartom claimed seven lives and demolished or damaged eighteen houses and eight outbuildings. Two bridges were destroyed on the Predel Pass road that links Bovec in Slovenia with Tarvisio in Italy. The damage amounted to 31 million euros [16].

Because television coverage aroused great public sympathy, access for locals was possible after a month and the area was completely open only three months after the disaster. Within this period, the streams in the slide area were regulated,

Figure 4:   Debris flow fan at the confluence of the Predelica (right) and Koritnica (left) streams in Log pod Mangartom (Photograph: Blaž Komac, November 19, 2000).

the ruins removed, a landslide alarm system installed, and temporary bridges built with the help of the Slovene army [3].

After the debris flow, the Parliament of the Republic of Slovenia passed a law on dealing with the consequences of larger landslides, and in 2003 adopted a location plan for managing the area of the debris flow. Barriers were constructed in the Predelica Valley, and fifteen replacement houses were built in Log pod Mangartom for residents whose property had been destroyed. The reconstruction work and the anticipated interventions evoked some criticism, in particular that access to the valley was forbidden for three months, the procedure for developing the national location plan led by the Ministry of Environment did not allow local residents sufficient opportunity to participate, the solutions proposed were not all professionally grounded, and additional houses had to be destroyed for the construction of a new concrete bridge in the village. Furthermore, the final decisions on the building of houses only began in 2004, so people with destroyed homes had to wait several years before the construction of new houses was allowed.

3   Conclusion

The Log pod Mangartom disaster was one of the largest in Slovenia in recent decades since it claimed seven lives. It was unexpected, even though there have been many landslides in the area. The debris flow revealed lacustrine chalk, which shows that major geomorphological events have occurred in the Koritnica

Valley in the past. These are also reflected in local site names such as "Meli," which means "scree" in English [5].

A similar event occurred almost three hundred years ago when a clay quarry was buried, resulting without a doubt in the cessation of pottery making in the village of Strmec na Predelu [5]. On August 26, 1891, "thick sand" destroyed a flourmill and sawmill at the confluence of the Predelica and Koritnica valleys. An innkeeper reported that the water carried away *"all the yard up to the corner of the house and buried half of my barn. On the other side it buried an entire house."* The disaster also carried away a house *"from which came neither soul nor sound..."* [22].

Figure 5:   The debris flow destroyed or damaged 18 houses and 8 outbuildings (Photograph: Matija Zorn, November 30, 2000).

Similar events have occurred along the nearby Ugovizza stream (for example end of August 2003) in the Val Canale valley in Italy where sources from the end of the 18th century report debris flows. On the basis of historical data that stretches back to the 16th century, it has been determined that larger such events have a return period of twenty-five years and smaller ones form three to six years [19].

A link exists between the increasing occurrence of debris flows in the American state of Virginia and the period when the climate changed to the extent that it enabled the frequent penetration of warm tropical air masses to the central part of the Appalachian Mountains. In the canyons of the California deserts, debris flows occur almost once every thirty to one hundred years [18].

The activity of debris flows in Slovenia's Alps is also an indicator of climate change. Debris flows were very frequent during the penultimate glacial period, in the interglacial period, and after the last glacial period. The sediment from debris

Figure 6:   Mount Mangart (in the middle behind; 2,679 m) with landslide on the left and debris flow fan in Log pod Mangartom on the right (Photograph: Matija Zorn, August 25, 2001).

flows then covered the greater part of the nearby Bovec basin [1] and there were frequent large rock falls in the Julian Alps [21]. In the Vipava Valley, there was a landslide with a volume of around 150 million cubic meters [15].

With this in mind, it will be in the greatest interest to observe the changing frequency of these events relative to climate change in the near future as well.

References

[1]   Bavec, M., Tulaczyk, S.M. Mahan, S.A. & Stock, G.M., Late Quaternary glaciation of the Upper Soča River Region (Southern Julian Alps, NW Slovenia). *Sedimentary geology* **165(3-4)**, pp. 265–283, 2004. doi:10.1016/j.sedgeo.2003.11.011

[2]   Komac, B., Geografski vidiki nesreče (Geographical aspects of the disaster). *Ujma* **14-15**, pp. 60–66, 2001.

[3]   Komac, B., Drobirski tok pod Mangartom (Debris flow below Mt. Mangart). *Vodniki Ljubljanskega geografskega društva 3*, ed. D. Kladnik, Založba ZRC: Ljubljana, pp. 95–106, 2003.

[4]   Komac, B. & Zorn, M., Recenti pobočni procesi v Zgornjem Posočju (Recent slope processes in the Upper Soča valley). *Geografski obzornik* **49(1)**, pp. 10–17, 2002.

[5]   Komac, B. & Zorn, M., *Pobočni procesi in človek (Slope processes and a man)*. Založba ZRC: Ljubljana, 2007.

[6]   Majes, B., Analiza plazu in možnosti njegove sanacije (Analysis of landslide and its rehabilitation). *Ujma* **14-15**, pp. 80–91, 2001.

[7]   Majes, B., Petkovšek, A. & Logar, J., Primerjava materialnih lastnosti drobirskih tokov iz plazov Stože, Slano blato in Strug (The comparison of material properties of debris flows from Stože, Slano blato and Strug landslides). *Geologija* **45(2)**, pp. 457–463, 2002.

[8]   Mikoš, M., Četina, M. & Brilly, M., Hydrologic conditions responsible for triggering the Stože landslide, Slovenia. *Engineering Geology* **73(3-4)**, pp. 193–213, 2004. doi:10.1016/j.enggeo.2004.01.011

[9]   Mikoš, M., Brilly, M., Fazarinc, R. & Ribičič, M., Sediment production and delivery from recent large landslides and earthquake-induced rock falls in the Upper Soča River Valley, Slovenia. *Engineering Geology* **86(2-3)**, pp. 1–13, 2006. doi:10.1016/j.enggeo.2006.02.015

[10] Natek, K., Komac, B. & Zorn, M., Mass movements in the Julian Alps (Slovenia) in the aftermath of the Easter earthquake on April 12, 1998. *Studia Geomorphologica Carpatho-Balcanica* **37**, pp. 29–43, 2003.

[11] Ogrin, D., Podnebni tipi v Sloveniji (Climate types in Slovenia.). *Geografski vestnik* **68**, pp. 39–56, 1996.

[12] Orožen Adamič, M. (ed.), *Poplave v Sloveniji (Floods in Slovenia)*. Ljubljana: Ministrstvo za obrambo Republike Slovenije, 1992.

[13] Pavšek, M., *Snežni plazovi v Sloveniji (Avalanches in Slovenia)*. Ljubljana: Založba ZRC, 2002.

[14] Petkovšek, A., Geološko geotehnične raziskave plazu (Geological-geotechnical investigations of the Stože landslide). *Ujma* **14-15**, pp. 109–117, 2001.

[15] Popit T. & Košir A., Pleistocenski plaz pri Selu v Vipavski dolini (Pleistocene landslide at Selo in the Vipava valley). *Geološki zbornik* **17**, pp. 133–138, 2003.

[16] Poročilo o uresničevanju Zakona o ukrepih za odpravo posledic plazu Stože v občini Bovec in plazov večjega obsega, nastalih na območju Republike Slovenije po 15. oktobru 2000. *Poročevalec Državnega zbora Republike Slovenije* **66(118)**, 2001.

[17] Ribičič, M., Značilnosti drobirskega toka Stože pod Mangartom (Debris flow at Log pod Mangartom). *Ujma* **14-15**, pp. 102–108, 2001.

[18] Ritter, D.F., Kochel, R.C. & Miller, J.R., *Process geomorphology*. Dubuque: Brown Publishers, 1995.

[19] Tropeano, D., Turconi, L. & Sanna, S., Debris flows triggered by the 29 august 2003 cloudburst in Val Canale, eastern Italian Alps. *International Congress Interpraevent* **1**, pp. 121–132, 2004

[20] Ulaga, F., Koncentracija suspendiranega gradiva v vodotokih (Suspended load concentration in Slovene streams). *Mesečni bilten* **7(11)**, pp. 37–39, 2000.

[21] Zorn, M., Rockfalls in Slovene Alps. *Acta geographica Slovenica* **42**, pp. 122–160, 2002.

[22] Zorn, M., Komac, B., Pobočni procesi in drobirski tok v Logu pod Mangartom (Slope processes and the debris flow in Log pod Mangartom). *Geografski vestnik* **74(1)**, pp. 9–23, 2002.

A case study on the occurrence of regional debris flow hazard in central Taiwan

C.-C. Lee[1], C.-Y. Ku[2,3], S.-M. Hsu[2], Y.-L. Chang[2] & S.-Y. Chi[2]
[1]National Chung Hsing University, Taiwan, R.O.C.
[2]Sinotech Engineering Consultants, Inc., Taiwan, R.O.C.
[3]National Taiwan Ocean University, Taiwan, R.O.C.

Abstract

Large-scale debris flow hazards occurred in Ta-Chia River watershed during typhoons that passed through Taiwan from 2001 to 2005 without forewarning. Especially, the Minduli typhoon event in 2004 hit Taiwan which caused severe property damage and inflicted heavy casualties. Though landslide-induced debris flows present a hazard that is being increasingly recognized, such a large-scale debris flow hazard in Ta-Chia River watershed still appears to be particular. Until now, few detailed case studies of regional debris flow hazards in Ta-Chia River watershed have been presented in the literature. In this paper, we present a detailed study on the occurrence of regional debris flow hazard in Ta-Chia River watershed and reveal the trigger mechanism of the landslide and debris flow. To explore the coupling between the Chi-Chi earthquake and sequential regional debris flow hazards in Ta-Chia River watershed, the remote sensing data, Digital Elevation Model (DEM), historical landslides, and rainfall data were adopted in this study. For characterizing temporal aspects of the hazard, aerial photographs and satellite images of multi-temporal stages were used. Spatial distribution of landslides and rainfall characteristics were also discussed. Our findings indicate that the regional debris flow hazards were mainly caused by the huge amount of sparsely deposited materials from landslides triggered by Chi-Chi earthquake. Rapidly increasing water pressure caused by typhoon events provided a powerful force that moved the sparsely deposited materials into gullies and then triggered the debris flow movement. A strong coupling between the spatial distribution of rainfalls and the occurrence of regional debris flows is also addressed.

Keywords: debris flow, landslide, rainfall intensity, Chi-Chi earthquake, Taiwan.

WIT Transactions on Engineering Sciences, Vol 60, © 2008 WIT Press
www.witpress.com, ISSN 1743-3533 (on-line)
doi:10.2495/DEB080141

1 Introduction

Observations of landslides and debris flows have been reported for many decades. Historically typhoon events with high-intensity, long-duration rainfall often triggered shallow, rapidly moving landslides, i.e. debris flows, resulting in casualties and property damage in Taiwan along the past decades. It is widely recognized that slope instability can be caused by increased subsurface pore pressures during periods of intense rainfall. A number of studies have demonstrated that rainfall-induced landslides can be transformed into debris flows as they move downslope.

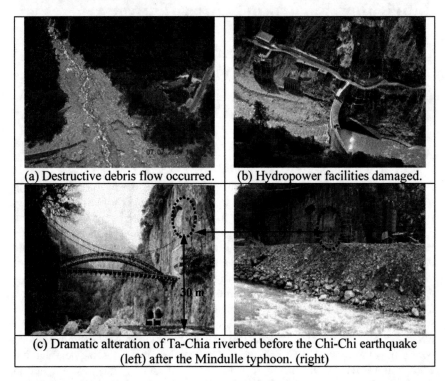

(a) Destructive debris flow occurred.　(b) Hydropower facilities damaged.

(c) Dramatic alteration of Ta-Chia riverbed before the Chi-Chi earthquake (left) after the Mindulle typhoon. (right)

Figure 1:　Debris flow hazards in the study area.

Large-scale debris flow hazards occurred in Ta-Chia River watershed during typhoons that passed through Taiwan from 2001 to 2005 without forewarning. Especially, the Minduli typhoon event in 2004 hit Taiwan which caused severe property damage and inflicted heavy casualties as shown in Figure 1. Though landslide-induced debris flows present a hazard that is being increasingly recognized, such a large-scale debris flow hazard in Ta-Chia River watershed still appears to be particular. On September 21, 1999, the Chi-Chi earthquake was triggered by the reactivation of the Chelungpu fault near Chi-Chi in central Taiwan. This earthquake triggered numerous landslides and severely disturbed montane slopes. However, the debris flow hazard did not appear in the first two years after this earthquake. Post-earthquake watershed restoration works progressed without disruptions until several typhoon events with intense rainfall, such as (1) Toraji in 2001, (2) Minduli in 2004, (3) Airi in 2004, and (4) Hytarng in 2005, hit Taiwan and triggered numerous debris flows in central Taiwan and caused significant property damage and inflicted heavy casualties in regional scale.

Until now, few detailed case studies of regional debris flow hazards in Ta-Chia River watershed have been presented in the literature. In this paper, we present a detailed study on the occurrence of regional debris flow hazard in Ta-Chia River watershed and reveal the trigger mechanism of the landslide and debris flow. To explore the coupling between the Chi-Chi earthquake and sequential regional debris flow hazards in Ta-Chia River watershed, the remote sensing data, Digital Elevation Model (DEM), historical landslides, and rainfall data were adopted in this study. For characterizing temporal aspects of the hazard, aerial photographs and satellite images of multi-temporal stages were adopted. Spatial distribution of landslides and rainfall characteristics were also discussed.

2 Study region

The study region includes a major river, named Ta-Chia river, one of the abundant water resources in central Taiwan as shown in Figure 2. The Ta-Chia river watershed area is about 1,236 km². The elevation of the highest mountain in the watershed is around 3,875 m. The river stretch extends 124 km from upstream to the sea. This river valley is notable because it incorporates the Central Cross Island road that links the east and west coasts of Taiwan across the Central Mountains. A series of significant hydroelectric schemes that extend along the length of the river, consisting of one high, concrete arch dam at Te-Chi, and a series of dams and hydropower stations were built in 1960s. There are

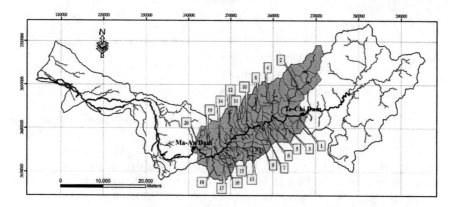

Figure 2: Study region and tributaries.

also many tributaries along the Ta-Chia river. In our study region, about 20 tributaries were found between Te-Chi dam and Ma-An dam. The area of our study region is 396.5 km^2. Since severe debris flow hazards were occurred in this region, the following discussion focused on it.

2.1 Geological setting

The study area consists of a steeply incised valley orientated approximately east-west in the eastern part of the Central Range. The geology consists of a series of interbedded Tertiary sandstones and slates, with occasional limestone bands. The geologic strata of Ta-Chia river are argillite, slate, quartzite, sandstone, siltstone and shale including Lushan Formation, Tatungshan Formation, Kankou Formation, Chiayang Formation, Szeleng Sandstone, Tachien Sandstone, Kuohsing Formation, Guandaoshan Formation, Jinshuei Formation and Jhuolan Formation as shown in Figure 3. The rock mass is extensively tectonically disrupted, with a high density of fractures and joints. The slope inclination in the watershed is ranging from 40 to 80 degrees.

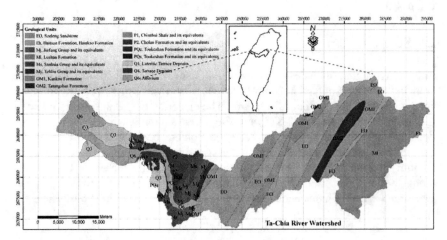

Figure 3:   Location of Ta-Chia river watershed in Taiwan and its geological map.

2.2 Major debris flow storm events in the study area

During 1996 to 2005, according to the Central Weather Bureau of Taiwan, the following storm events including typhoon Herb in 1996, typhoon Toraji in 2001, typhoon Minduli in 2004, typhoon Airi in 2004, and Hytarng in 2005 have hit the study area. Within this period, the Chi-Chi earthquake on 21 September 1999 which is the largest in Taiwan for 50 years, was also occurred. This typhoon-earthquake-typhoon sequence represents a natural experiment that provides quantitative information about the impact of a large earthquake on landslides and transfer of sediment to debris flows.

3   Occurrence of regional debris flow hazards

3.1   Landslide mapping

Shallow landsliding is the most common landslide type on steep natural hillslopes in the Ta-Chia river watershed. Multi-temporal remote sensing data including aerial-photograph and SPOT satellite imaginary were used for landslide mapping. For characterizing temporal aspects of the debris flows, remote sensing data include aerial photographs and satellite images of five temporal stages which are the stage before and after Chi-Chi earthquake, the stage after typhoon Toraji, the stage after typhoon Minduli, the stage after typhoon Airi and Hytarng. Table 1 shows before and after the Chi-Chi earthquake (1989) the landslide rates are 0.68% and 7.54% respectively. After typhoon Toraji in 2001, typhoon Minduli in 2004, and typhoon Airi in 2004, the landslide rates are 6.05%, 7.80%, and, 6.92% respectively. Comparing the landslide rate from these events, it is found that the Chi-Chi earthquake has caused significant landslides in the study region.

Table 1:   Landslide area mapping from multi-temporal remote sensing data.

	Landslide area (km^2)	Landslide rate	Increase area (km^2)	Increase rate
Before Chi-Chi earthquake	2.69	0.68%	~	~
After Chi-Chi earthquake	29.91	7.54%	28.34	7.15%
After typhoon Toraji	23.99	6.05%	6.68	1.68%
After typhoon Minduli	30.94	7.80%	14.04	3.54%
After typhoon Airi	27.43	6.92%	6.68	1.69%

Note: The landslide rate is the landslide area divided by watershed area (396.5 km2).

Furthermore, we computed the new landslides triggered by each event and found that the increase rates of slope failures occurred by these events are 7.15%, 1.68%, 3.54%, and 1.69% for four events including the Chi-Chi earthquake,

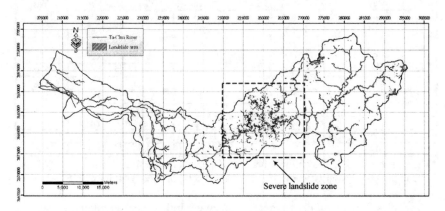

Figure 4:   Spatial distribution of landslide areas.

typhoon Toraji, typhoon Minduli, and typhoon Airi, respectively. Accordingly, we have revealed that the Chi-Chi earthquake with the landslide increase rate of 7.15% is the major event for inducing the landslides and typhoon Minduli with the landslide increase rate of 3.54% is the second. From the results of landslide mapping as shown in Figure 4, we found that the landslides were most located in the areas between Te-Chi dam and Ma-An dam.

3.2 Characteristics of major debris flows

Table 2 shows the occurrence record of the debris flows in the study region. Before the Chi-Chi earthquake, no observations of debris flows have been reported for decades. After the Chi-Chi earthquake and the first typhoon Toraji hit the region in 2001, three branch rivers (# 13, #14, and #17) with the occurrence of debris flow have been reported. Severe debris flow hazards have been reported during the typhoon Minduli in 2004. The occurrence of debris flow was found in almost all of the branches, except one in the downstream. The following two typhoon events such as Airi in 2004 and Hytarng in 2005 also moved huge amount of debris sediment from these branch rivers into the main Ta-Chia river.

Table 2: Occurrence record of the debris flows.

Branch river #[1]	Watershed area	Watershed slope	Branch river slope	Landslide rate (%)	Occurrence of debris flow[2]	Occurrence of debris flow[3]	Occurrence of debris flow[4]	Occurrence of debris flow[5]
1	8.86	33.8	11.5	10.26	No	Yes	Yes	Yes
2	88.24	33.5	3.2	4.87	No	Yes	Yes	Yes
3	13.74	37.0	20.2	17.83	No	Yes	Yes	Yes
4	36.30	35.5	6.6	16.82	No	Yes	Yes	Yes
5	1.98	40.0	24.6	40.73	No	Yes	Yes	Yes
6	7.35	36.1	13.9	17.57	No	Yes	Yes	Yes
7	3.49	40.4	21.0	32.50	No	Yes	Yes	Yes
8	22.12	33.2	7.1	18.68	No	Yes	Yes	Yes
9	9.70	35.9	13.1	24.21	No	Yes	Yes	Yes
10	6.76	37.2	15.2	29.73	No	Yes	Yes	Yes
11	12.12	32.7	6.8	9.56	No	Yes	Yes	Yes
12	18.57	31.1	5.6	10.65	No	Yes	Yes	Yes
13	31.09	34.4	7.6	12.34	Yes	Yes	Yes	Yes
14	3.66	32.1	9.2	21.27	Yes	Yes	Yes	Yes
15	3.75	32.5	14.3	15.44	No	Yes	Yes	Yes
16	0.57	32.6	21.7	11.10	No	Yes	Yes	Yes
17	7.76	30.8	10.0	7.88	Yes	Yes	Yes	Yes
18	20.50	28.9	4.4	11.64	No	Yes	Yes	Yes
19	20.89	30.4	6.2	11.34	No	Yes	Yes	Yes
20	5.98	28.2	9.5	4.23	No	No	No	No

[1] The branch river # is shown in Figure 2. [2] After typhoon Toraji in 2001. [3] After typhoon Minduli in 2004. [4] After typhoon Airi in 2004. [5] After typhoon Hytarng in 2005.

A debris flow is usually triggered by heavy rainfall over mountainous areas. It is made up of mud, soils, gravels, rocks, and water. Solids or soils on steep slopes slide downward due to weathering processes and mechanical influence such as gravity. From the occurrence of the debris flow hazard in the study area, it is obvious that the weathering process is not the major cause for creating such a large scale of the debris flow hazard. The mechanical influence from the Chi-Chi earthquake disturbed montane slopes, thus setting the conditions for the occurrence of the regional debris flows.

3.3 Analysis of rainfall characteristics

Precipitation exerts two controls on the Ta-Chia river watershed. One is as a trigger of landslide and therefore as materials on the occurrence of debris flows. The other is by providing water, therefore enhancing the mobility of debris flows. To explore the trigger mechanisms of the typhoon-earthquake-typhoon sequence, analysis of rainfall characteristics was conducted in this study. Precipitation data from more than 20 rainfall stations operated by Water Resources Agency of the Taiwan Ministry of Economic Affairs and other government agencies in the watershed were adopted for conducting the rainfall frequency analysis. The results of the frequency analysis were represented as the return period of rainfall. The return period of a storm event is the expected value of its average value measured over a very large number of occurrences. Table 3 is the comparison of accumulated rainfall of 1, 3, 6, 12, and 24 hours for Toraji, Minduli, Airi, and Hytarng typhoon events and the computed return period of rainfall for 2, 10, 25, 50, and 100 years on the upper Gu-Gang rainfall station. From the frequency analysis, we have found that the 1 and 3 hours accumulated rainfall of typhoon Minduli are over the 50-year return period of rainfall. Typhoon Minduli with heavy rainfalls brought sufficient water transporting significant amounts of sparsely deposited debris from landslides in upland into gullies and then induced the regional debris flow hazards.

Table 3: Comparison of accumulated rainfall for major typhoon events and the return period of rainfall on the upper Gu-Gang rainfall station.

Accumulated rainfall	Toraji	Return period	Minduli	Return period	Airi	Return period	Hytarng	Return period
1 hour (mm)	77.5	75 (10 yrs) 85 (25yrs)	94.5	92 (50 yrs) 99 (100 yrs)	56.5	50 (2 yrs) 66 (5 yrs)	28.5	50 (2 yrs)
3 hours (mm)	173.5	174 (25yrs)	199	191 (50 yrs) 208 (100 yrs)	158	149 (10 yrs) 174 (25 yrs)	63	92 (2 yrs)
6 hours (mm)	259.5	226 (10 yrs) 268 (25 yrs)	271	268 (25 yrs) 298 (50 yrs)	297.5	298 (50 yrs)	117.5	133 (2 yrs)
12 hours (mm)	317	283 (5 yrs) 341 (10 yrs)	394.5	341 (10 yrs) 411 (25 yrs)	426	411 (25 yrs) 461 (50 yrs)	196	193 (2 yrs)
1 day (mm)	344.5	295 (2 yrs) 447 (5 yrs)	603	545(10 yrs) 636 (20 yrs)	504	420 (5 yrs) 513 (10 yrs)	452.5	420 (5 yrs) 513 (10 yrs)

Further analysis also conducted to reveal the spatial distribution of rainfall in the study region. We plotted contours of the 200-year return period of rainfall for each gauging station in Ta-Chia river watershed as shown in Figure 5. Results demonstrated that the spatial distribution of the precipitation in the study region mainly concentrated around the upper Gu-Gang rainfall station.

From the results of landslide mapping as shown in Figure 4, we found that the landslides were most located in the areas between Te-Chi dam and Ma-An dam. Comparing Figures 4 and 5, it is found that the regional debris flow hazards in Ta-Chia river watershed are strong related to the spatial distribution of rainfalls.

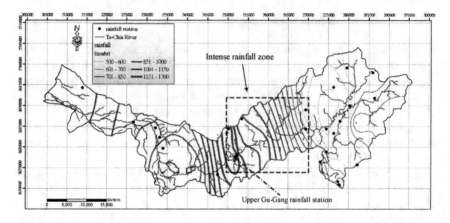

Figure 5: Spatial distribution of rainfall characteristics.

4 Formation of debris flow

It is widely recognized that slope instability can be caused by increased subsurface pore pressures during periods of intense rainfall, which reduce the shear strength of slope materials. A number of recent studies have demonstrated that rainfall-induced landslides can be transformed into debris flows as they move downslope. Figure 6 shows multi-temporal aerial-photographs of the formation of a debris flow. In this figure, the four stages including before and after Chi-Chi earthquake, after typhoon Toraji, and after typhoon Minduli of aerial-photographs were presented. Before the Chi-Chi earthquake (1998), it was clear that the branch # 14 was just a regular gully that the water flow only presents in precipitation. In 1999 (after the Chi-Chi earthquake), landslides initiated from the source areas but no debris flow occurred. In 2001, typhoon Toraji hit this region. The appearance of water flow during storm precipitation is advantageous for mixing with accumulated material from source areas to stir the progression of a beginning landslide into a debris flow. Field reconnaissance of this study area revealed that the trigger mechanism of this debris flow took place in two stages: the primary slope failure was due to the Chi-Chi earthquake from the source area. The hydraulic movement was transferred to the landslide mass of the source area flowing into brook track, following slope surface exposure to the action of running water.

Debris flows are commonly triggered by the sudden increase in pore water pressure on the material. This rapid increase in pore water pressure, however, may not always be attributable to the infiltration of precipitation. In this study case, the debris flow resulted from the mixing of rock fragments, fine fractions and water, moving together down gully, and finally deposited in downstream of the gully in which the slope angles for each phase is ranging from about 35, 11.5, and 9.5 degrees, respectively.

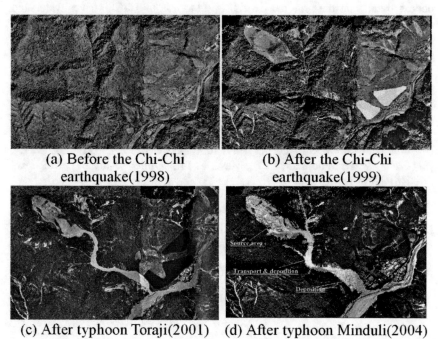

(a) Before the Chi-Chi earthquake(1998)   (b) After the Chi-Chi earthquake(1999)

(c) After typhoon Toraji(2001)   (d) After typhoon Minduli(2004)

Figure 6:   Trigger mechanism of the debris flow occurrence in the study area.

5 Conclusions

Large-scale debris flow hazards occurred in Ta-Chia River watershed during typhoons that passed through Taiwan from 2001 to 2005 which caused severe property damage and inflicted heavy casualties. In this paper, we present a detailed study on the occurrence of regional debris flow hazards in Ta-Chia River watershed and reveal the trigger mechanism and geomorphological evolution of the landslide and debris flow. Findings from this study are described as following.

Shallow landsliding is the most common landslide type on steep natural hillslopes in the Ta-Chia river watershed. A number of studies have demonstrated that rainfall-induced landslides can be transformed into debris flows as they move downslope. In this study, we have revealed that the Chi-Chi earthquake with the landslide increase rate of 7.15% is the major event for inducing the landslides and typhoon Minduli with the landslide increase rate of 3.54% is the second in the study area. From the occurrence of the debris flow hazards in the study area, it is obvious that the weathering process is not the major cause for creating such a large scale of the debris flow hazard. The mechanical influence from the Chi-Chi earthquake disturbed montane slopes, thus setting the conditions for the occurrence of the regional debris flows. Analysis results from the spatial distribution of rainfall in the study region demonstrated that the regional debris flow hazards in Ta-Chia river watershed are strong related to the spatial distribution of rainfalls.

References

[1] Taiwan Power Company, Investigation and Strategy Study of Landslide and Debris flows in Ta-Chia river Basin Between Te-Chi and Ma-An, 2006.
[2] Keefer, D. K., Wilson, R. C., Mark, R. K., Brab, E. E., Brown, W. M., Ellen, S. D., Harp, E. L., Wieczorek, G. F., Alger, C. S., and Zatkin, R. S., Real-time landslide warning during heavy rainfall,, Science 238, 921–925, 1987.
[3] Chow, V. T., Maidment, D. R., Mays, L. W., Applied Hydrology, McGraw-Hill, New York, 1988.
[4] Iverson, R.M., Landslide trigger by rain infiltration. Water Resour Res. 36(7): 1897–1910, 2000.
[5] Maleta J.-P., D. Laigleb, A. Remaîtrea, O. Maquaire, Triggering conditions and mobility of debris flows associated to complex earthflows, Geomorphology 66 215–235, 2005.
[6] Chen, Hongey, Dadson, Simon, Chi, Yi-Guan, Recent rainfall-induced landslides and debris flow in northern Taiwan, 77, 112–125, Geomorphology, 2006.

Section 4
Sediment transport and debris flow including woody debris.
Special session organised by D. De Wrachien and M. A. Lenzi

Special session organized by D. De Wrachien & M. A. Lenzi

Scope aims and topics

The terms resource and natural disaster are a reflection of mankind's perception of natural systems. When man recognises a natural system as useful, it becomes a resource whereas if it is potentially harmful, it is seen as a danger. In the absence of human settlement, however, there are neither resources nor dangers, but merely natural systems [1].

In this context a disaster can be defined as an event where damage exceeds the capacity of the affected society to recover by its own means. This implies that there are local disasters that can be dealt with by regional help and that there are regional or even national disasters that require national or international help. This definition does not implicitly include the terms "frequent" or "exceptional" but merely implies that the size of a disaster is related to the specific society affected and underlines the fact that the weaker are usually the most severely affected by natural disasters [2]. Water-forest related natural disasters – to which the large woody debris accumulations (LWD), debris and hyper-concentrated flows belong – are mainly the result of physical processes, which cause disasters when they interact with human activities. The mitigation of such phenomena could, therefore, be achieved by reducing this interaction, by altering the natural system, the human system of both.

The trend of increase in the environmental and economic impacts of natural disasters, and in particular the water-forest related ones, has continued during the past half century. Over the last 30 years, although the number of lives lost by natural disasters has declined, the number of people affected and estimated economic losses have been steadily increasing.

LWD, debris and hyper-concentrated flows result from the interaction of hydrological processes with geological process and are triggered when soils get saturated and the stability of the slope is no longer maintained. These flows are among the most destructive of all water-related disasters. They mainly affect mountain areas in a wide range of morphoclimatic environments and in recent years have attracted more a more attention from the scientific and professional

WIT Transactions on Engineering Sciences, Vol 60, © 2008 WIT Press
www.witpress.com, ISSN 1743-3533 (on-line)
doi:10.2495/DEB080151

communities and concern from the public awareness, due to the increasing frequency with which they occur and the death toll they claim.

Higher population pressures on natural resources in hazard-prone areas and development of activities that have the potential to increase the magnitude of hazard call for improvements in the criteria used to identify debris flow risk areas and to design prevention and mitigation measures. There is need to take into account risks emanating from these events into the development process in general and forest, land and water resources management in particular. Sustainable development should take account of hydrological variability through appropriate risk management policies in all climatic zones and hydrological regimes. Integrated forest, land and water resources management should incorporate risk management principles in dealing with extreme hydrological events like debris and hyper-concentrated flows.

The identification of effective procedures aimed at evaluating the probability of extreme hydrological events producing socio-economic damages to human settlements has turned out to be an essential component of the forest, land and water planning and management process.

It is worth noting that, whilst in the past the concept of risk was primarily intended as a measure of the probability of a system's failure, it has assumed nowadays a more complex meaning. The risk should be, in fact, considered as a combination of both the probability and the magnitude of the consequence (e.g. the effect) of a system's failure and, therefore, as the expectation of the consequence, taking into account all significant hazards and all significant mechanisms of failure [3].

In this context, the object of risk analysis changes too, depending on both the system to be considered and the goals to be pursued. The risk analysis procedure should, therefore, consist of two different and consequential phases: a first phase aimed at classifying the object of the analysis and at defining the variables on which the risk depends, and a second phase aimed at specifying the conditions and the modes of the system failure.

This concept leads to a new integrated risk management approach which comprises the systematic process, administrative decisions, organisation, operational skills and abilities to implement policies, strategies, and coping capacities of the society and communities to lessen the impact of natural hazards and related environmental disasters [4].

This approach provides measures for preventing a hazard turning into a natural disaster and consists of systematic actions in a cycle of preparedness, response and recovery that should form part of an integrated forest, land and water resources management procedure. Preparedness consists of preventive and precautionary measures to prepare for an event before it occurs. It aims at minimizing the effect of development activities on accentuating the magnitude of hazards, reducing the exposure to natural hazards and minimising the socio-economic vulnerability of people and material assets exposed to these hazards. Response deals with measures that limit the effects of exposure to a hazard, and its duration. It mainly focuses on alerting potential affected people, rescuing victims and providing assistance in case of need. It also includes immediate measures to prevent further adverse impacts and provisional reconditioning of important infrastructures affected. The recovery phase aims at enabling the economic and social activities to return to normal with a minimum delay. It also involves the analysis of the disaster in order to learn lessons and ingrate corrective measures into prevention and preparedness plans. These actions are taken depending on the conditions of risk and social, economic and physical setting, with major focus on reducing the vulnerability that has to be addressed through local actions to overcome global challenges.

It is important to understand that while our planning capabilities, technological tools and methods might be adequate, our capacity to enforce these plans may be affected by political considerations and thus become closer to nonexistent. It is worth stressing that the effectiveness of the risk management cycle in reducing risks and damages depends on the political will to apply the risk management principles in development planning, the existence of a chain of well-defined institutional responsibilities and a democratic process of consultation and social control with effective governance. Well-designed prevention and mitigation measures should not only deal with day to day operation, but must also include risk analysis and suitable measures to cope with extraordinary disturbances. To this end, worst scenario emergency planning for such likely events is essential. Monitoring, forecasting and early warning play a pivotal role in the risk management cycle. Regular monitoring of elements that constitute forest-water-related hazards is crucial during the preparedness, response and reconstruction phases. Unpredictability of climatic extremes for specific regions and their extent is the vital gap in the knowledge on climate change, which needs to be addressed. Advanced scientific research should be applied in monitoring forest-water-related hazards through appropriate networks of climatic, hydrological and geological parameters.

Developments in remote sensing, satellite communication and information technology should be used for improving monitoring and developing mathematical models for forecasting and early warning of impending hazards. The challenge before the international community is to support these activities, particularly in developing countries, where resources for such actions are limited.

Greater research needs to be directed towards understanding the nature of regional climates, hydrological regimes, geological processes, including their variability and potential for change. Such knowledge is essential in order to estimate the potential frequency of natural hazards and the options for adaptation that are available. Early warning is effective only if it reaches the affected people who have to respond to such a situation. Science and technology should try to break the barrier of financial resources to enable such warning to reach even the remotest corners of the affected areas.

Field studies are probably the most difficult and costly tasks within this integrated approach. The difficulties encountered are connected to the complexity of the phenomena investigated and the difficulty of direct observation. The exceptional conditions in which such extreme events occur do not generally permit a sufficient number of observations for the same type of territorial reality to work out the peculiar behavioural laws for that area.

Reference to different territorial situations also highlights another problem: that of the homogeneity of data given the substantial territorial peculiarity in which the phenomena occur.

In relation with this Special Session, large woody debris accumulations, debris and hyper-concentrated flows are a familiar hazard in mountain areas and regularly cause both loss of life, livestock and property and disruption of communications. The potential for such losses is growing as the mountain areas are increasingly developed and insurance claims, as a result of this threat, are steadily rising. Further, the development itself (e.g. construction of roads and recreational areas, tourist trade) can increase the incidence of LWD, hyper-concentrated and debris flows by changing their topographic, features and soil and vegetation controls. Hazard assessment is therefore increasingly required in land use planning in mountain environments.

The ideal sequence that should be pursued in the approach to the difficult problem of the management and hazard mitigation of LWD, hyper-concentrated and debris flows can be outlined as follows:

1) first, a systematic collection of field data should be carried out in order to provide a large base of reliable data that could allow a better knowledge of the existing risk trends and a deeper understanding of the mechanics of the phenomena, along with their general behaviour and effects;
2) secondly, effective mathematical models, which strongly depend on data and measurements collected and performed in the field for their calibration and design, should be constantly developed, updated when needed, tested and applied;
3) hazard mapping techniques and identification of possible scenarios, which need reliable models to be effective and sound, should then be set up;
4) on the basis of the knowledge achieved in the previous steps, the best mitigation solutions should be identified, designed and built up;
5) finally a program of systematic observations on the sites, where risk has been mitigated, should be planned and carried out to detect any shortcoming and test the efficiency of the investigations.

Each of the above studies and investigations needs improvements and depends, to achieve them, on improvements in the other fields. As an example, current monitoring procedures need, in general, to be improved to be able to perform measurements in all the different field conditions. Improving measurement and documentation procedures would provide a better knowledge and ideas for new and more advanced models. The application of existing models based on the data collected in the field and the development of reliable new ones would allow, on one hand, to better focus what to observe in the field and, on the other hand, improve both mitigation methodologies and measures and hazard mapping procedures. The field application of these latter would then identify new parameters to be measured and introduced in the models. From all these activities would emerge the best mitigating solutions to be applied.

In this Special Session, particular attention will be given to both field data acquisition-monitoring approaches for sediment transport, LWD, hyper-concentrated and debris flows, and to the modelling and hazard assessment. Also the discussion of case study of catchments located in Italy and Southern Andes (Chile and Argentina) will be part of the Session.

References

[1]   Lorenzini, G. and Mazza M. 2004 Debris Flows. Phenomenology and Rheological Modelling .Wit press, Southampton, UK

[2]   4th World Water Forum 2006 –Framework theme 5

[3]   Meadcroft et al .1996. Development of new risk assessment procedures for coastal structures. In Advances in coastal structures and breakwaters. T. Thelford (Editor), London, UK

[4]   International Strategy for Disaster Reduction (ISDR) 2004. Terminology: Basic terms of disaster reduction

D. De Wrachien

M. A. Lenzi

Sediment transport monitoring in a Northern Puglia watershed

F. Gentile, T. Bisantino, R. Corbino, F. Milillo, G. Romano
& G. Trisorio Liuzzi
PROGESA Department, University of Bari, Bari, Italy

Abstract

The main torrents in Northern Apulia (Southern Italy) are characterised by a considerable suspended sediment transport that occurs during intense rainfall events. In this paper an experimental activity of sediment transport monitoring is described. A continuous measuring station located in the Carapelle torrent is equipped with a dual function optical immersion probe (turbidity/sediment). The probe has been tested with laboratory and field experiments carried out to verify the instrument's functional capabilities and to assess the relationship between optical and gravimetric data. Monitored data have then been used to analyze the sediment transport at event scale in view to estimate the sediment balance in the watershed.

Keywords: continuous river monitoring, sediment transport, turbidimeter.

1 Introduction

The sediment transport processes that affect the torrents originating from Subappennino dauno and crossing the alluvial valley of Tavoliere are mainly characterised by suspended materials. The Hydrological Service of Apulia Region measured the suspended load of these water courses during the period 1933–1989. After 1989 the monitoring system was interrupted.

In these torrents Marchi *et al* [1] found a close correlation between discharges and sediment loads. This is quite consistent with what observed by other authors who showed that the most of the annual suspended sediment is transported during the flood events, Walling *et al* [2]. During flood events the relationship between the suspended sediment concentration and the discharge is not linear

WIT Transactions on Engineering Sciences, Vol 60, © 2008 WIT Press
www.witpress.com, ISSN 1743-3533 (on-line)
doi:10.2495/DEB080161

and often presents a hysteretic loop. Analyzing the shapes of such relationships it is possible to identify the sediment sources, Williams [3], Lenzi and Marchi [4].

To accurately estimate the sediment transport during floods it is necessary to sample frequently or to set up a continuous measuring system, Lewis [5], Lewis [6]. Based on such considerations an experimental station was set up to measure the suspended sediment transport in the Carapelle stream (Basin area: 506 km^2). This station is equipped with a remote data transmission, ultrasound stage meter and a stage recorder. In addition, an infrared optic probe has been set up for the continuous measurement of the suspended sediment concentration, Bisantino *et al* [7].

The probe was preliminary tested in laboratory using mixtures of varying granulometric concentration to evaluate its functional capacity and to assess the effects of the different solid fractions on the measurements, Gentile *et al* [8]. Afterwards, the instrument was tested in the field through a calibration stage and the verification of the instrument housing. The most relevant flood events were then considered and the suspended sediment concentration, monitored at half-hourly scale, was plotted versus discharge to analyze the sediment transport dynamic.

2 Experimental station measuring suspended sediment concentration

The experimental station measuring suspended sediment concentration is located in the Carapelle torrent (at Ordona-Castelluccio Dei Sauri bridge), one of the main in Northern Apulia, fig. 1, tab.1. The torrent originates in the Apennine mountains and crosses the Tavoliere flood plain before flowing into the Adriatic

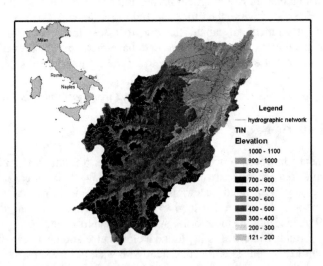

Figure 1:   The Carapelle watershed with mouth at the sediment transport experimental station.

Table 1:   Main characteristics of the Carapelle watershed.

Watershed area	A	506.2 km^2
Average altitude	H_m	466 m a.s.l.
Main channel length	L	52.16 km
Main channel slope	i_c	16.3%
Mean watershed slope	i_w	8.2%

sea. The watershed is characterised by clayey-sandy Plio-Pleistocene sediments in the alluvial fan and by flyschoid formations in the mountainous areas, which are subject to erosion. The plain and the low hilly areas are mainly used for olive growing, whereas the higher slopes are occupied by woods and pasture. The climate is typically Mediterranean, with rainfalls ranging from 450 to 800 mm/year and average temperatures ranging from 10 to16 °C.

The experimental sediment transport station is equipped with an infrared optical probe (Hach-Lange SOLITAX Hs-line), chosen in view of its sensitivity to the grain size distribution of the particles that characterise the suspended material. The probe has a dual function: it measures turbidity, when only the nephelometric photodetector is active, or suspended sediment when the backscattering photodetector also works.

The instrument is housed in a tube to protect it from the impact of any flowing coarse material and from any potential measuring errors caused by incident radiant energy straying into the infrared field, fig. 2.

Figure 2:   Sediment transport measuring station, optical probe housing and data acquisition system.

3   Functional characteristics of the optical probe: laboratory testing stage

During the experimental laboratory phase, the instrument was checked to evaluate its functionality in the two operating modes (turbidity and suspended sediment), both in homogenous granulometric mixtures and varying ratios between sandy and fine fraction. The instrument was analysed using a heterogeneous sample of material taken from the riverbed of the Carapelle stream. The material contained 87.5% of sand, 8.8% of silt and 3.7% of clay. The probe was fixed into an electromagnetic stirrer while Imhoff cones were used to separate the sediment fractions from the mixtures, fig. 3.

During the first stage, the material was divided into two samples: the first sample was oven-dried and used to make up 20 mixtures of homogeneous granulometry, in a set range of concentrations. The second sample, kept in naturally wet conditions, was used to make up 11 mixtures in which the concentrations were not predefined, although they were later established through a gravimetrical method. During the second stage the material was sifted (d=0.063 mm - UNI, BS Standards) to separate the sand fraction from the fine one (silt and clay) and used to prepare 36 mixtures of known concentration but different granulometric composition.

Figure 3: Laboratory equipment.

Using the probe in turbidity mode (*single photo detector*), a blindness effect has been observed (I stage) and, for very fine sediment, this effect occurs also for low sediment concentrations (II stage). In suspended sediment mode (*ratio detection system*) a first order relationship between measured and observed data was achieved (I stage); the curve slope increases with the fine fraction (II stage), fig. 4.

This result allows one to use a unique conversion factor for mixtures having the same grain size and different sediment concentrations. The results of this experimental phase have shown that, for the measurement of the suspended sediment transport, a combined system of photodetectors should be preferred. Measurements made with only one single photo detector are imprecise and non-linear due to the beam reduction process.

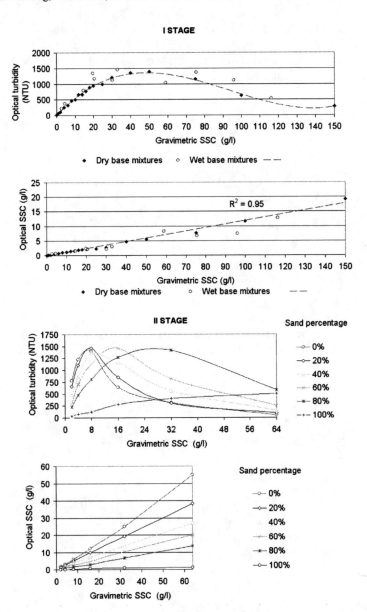

Figure 4:   Results of the laboratory experimental stages: existing relationships between the optical and the gravimetric data.

4   Field calibration stage

The instrument field testing was carried out in order to validate the results obtained during the laboratory study and, in particular, to confirm the existence of a linear relationship between the data measured by the instrument and the gravimetric data. Eight flood events were monitored and 65 turbid samples were collected using the "Magistrato" sampler, fig. 5. The instrument belongs to the "thief sampler" category, Holmes *et al* [9], and consists of a horizontal Van Dorn bottle closed by a float mechanism.

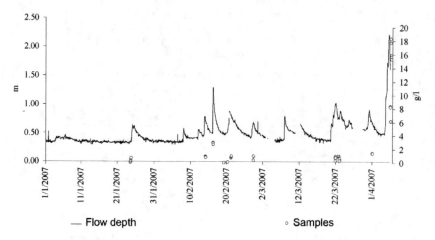

— Flow depth   ○ Samples

Figure 5:   Flow depth series and suspended sediments concentrations of the samples collected in the Carapelle stream during the 2006–2007 season.

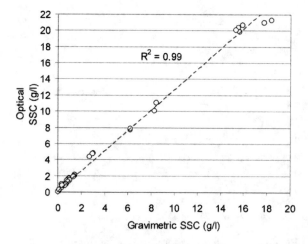

Figure 6:   Linear relationship existing between the optical suspended sediment concentration (SSC) measured in field and the gravimetric data.

Seventeen pairs of samples were taken outside and inside the tube in order to check the instrument lodging. Their sediment samples were then compared to evaluate the occurrence of any alterations caused by the protective tube. The external concentrations proved to be equal to the internal ones ($R^2=1$), and the samples taken from both positions have been considered as part of the dataset used during the calibration stage.

The samples collected during the flood events mainly consisted of fine materials: the first 28 samples, joined together, contained 9.4% of sand, 32.9% of silt and 57.7% of clay.

The sediment concentrations of all the samples proved to be correlated with the data measured by the instrument, as shown in figure 6. In the range of the monitored discharges the results confirmed the existence of a linear relationship between the gravimetric and the optical data.

5   Analysis of flood events

During the monitoring season, four significant events, having continuous data and absence of anomalies in the time series, have been selected. The data, registered at half-hourly scale, have been used to analyze the relationships, existing during the flood events, between the sediment concentration (SSC) and the discharge (Q_l). The results underline the existence of a hysteretic loop between sediment concentration and discharge, as shown in figure 7.

The loop-shaped curves, existing between SSC and Q_l, depend on the sediment availability that derives from sediment supply and/or from possible sediment deposits, Williams [3].

In the clockwise loop a rapid increase of the suspended sediment at the beginning of the flood event occurs for the presence of available sediment in the water course. If the sediment concentration decreases before the falling limb of the hydrograph, the sediment source areas can be considered limited. In the counterclockwise loop, instead, the sediment source areas are mainly located on hill slopes and the material moves slower than the peak discharge, Lenzi and Marchi [4].

In the first three events the sediment concentration decreases after the peak discharge (counterclockwise loop). This behaviour can be explained in terms of distance crossed by the sediment up to the measuring station during the events, Brasington and Richards [10].

The most intense event, that of April 5, is instead characterized by a clockwise loop. The advance of the sediment concentration peak can be explained because the sediment availability decreases during the event. This type of loop frequently occurs at the end of the rainy season and it is influenced by the availability of the sediments produced by the previous floods, Campbell [11].

The rate of transport changes from the falling limb to the rising limb of the hydrographs and this effect is induced by the unsteadiness of the flow, De Sutter *et al* [12].

6   Conclusions

In this paper the results of sediment transport monitoring study in a Northern Apulia torrent are reported. The adopted instrument is an optical immersion probe which measures the turbidity or the concentration of suspended solids.

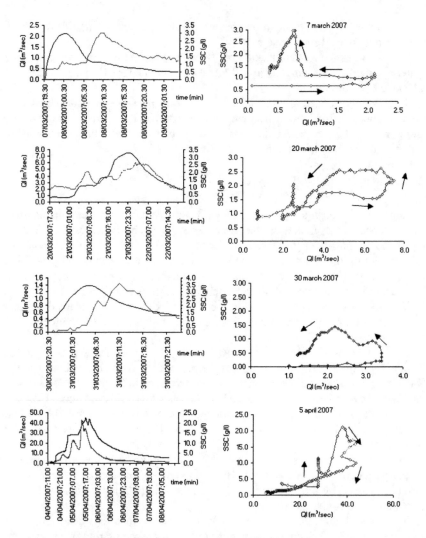

Figure 7: Relationships between the suspended sediment concentration (SSC) and the discharge (Q_l) during four significant flood events in the Carapelle stream.

The instrument was laboratory tested and the results showed that a combined photodetector system produced the best results, because a linear relationship between the optical and the gravimetric data was observed. Furthermore, with equal levels of concentration, the measurement tended to increase together with the fine fraction.

The field testing stage confirmed the results achieved in the laboratory, evidencing the linear relationship between the optical measurement of solid sediment transport and the gravimetric data measured on the turbidity samples. The instrument housing did not interfere the measuring process.

Four flood events were analysed to investigate the relationship between suspended sediment (SSC) concentration and discharge (Q_l) in unsteady flows. The SSC-Q_l curves revealed that in the Carapelle stream both the clockwise and counterclockwise loops are possible and can be related to the event intensity and to the sediment supply.

References

[1] Marchi, L., Trisorio-Liuzzi, & G., Zanframundo, P., *Analisi dei deflussi torbidi nei piccoli bacini del Sub- Appennino dauno.* Quaderni di Idronomia Montana, 6:95-121, 1986.

[2] Walling, D.E., Webb, B.W., & Woodward, J.C., *Some sampling considerations in the design of effective strategies for monitoring sediment-associated transport.* IAHS Spec. Publ. 210, 279–288, 1992.

[3] Williams, G.P., *Sediment concentration versus water discharge during single hydrologic events in rivers.* Journal of Hydrology 111:89–106, 1989.

[4] Lenzi, M. A., & Marchi, L., *Suspended sediment load during floods in a small stream of the Dolomites northeastern Italy.* Catena 39: 267–282, 2000.

[5] Lewis, J., *Turbidity-controlled suspended sediment sampling for runoff-event load estimation.* Water Resour. Res. 32(7): 2299-2310, 1996.

[6] Lewis, J., *Turbidity-controlled sampling for suspended sediment load estimation.* In: Bogen, J. Tharan Fergus and Des Walling (eds.), Erosion and Sediment Transport Measurement in Rivers: Technological and Methodological Advances (Proc. Oslo Workshop, 19-20 June 2002). IAHS Publ. 283: 13-20, 2003.

[7] Bisantino, T., Corbino, R., Gentile, F., Grittani, A., Milillo, F., Romano, G., Trisorio Liuzzi, G., & Zanframundo, P., *Monitoraggio del trasporto solido nei bacini della Puglia settentrionale tra il Candelaro e l'Ofanto.* Quaderni di Idronomia Montana 26: 193-204, 2006.

[8] Gentile, F., Bisantino, T., Milillo, F., Romano, G., & Trisorio Liuzzi, G., *Caratteristiche funzionali di una sonda a raggi infrarossi per la misura del trasporto solido in sospensione nei corsi d'acqua.* Quaderni di Idronomia Montana 27:421-432, 2007.

[9] Holmes, R. R., Jr., Terrio, P. J., Harris, M. A., & Mills, P. C., *Introduction to field methods for hydrologic and environmental studies.* U.S. Geological Survey, Open-File Report 01-50, Urbana, Illinois, 245 pp. http://onlinepubs.er.usgs.gov/djvu/OFR/2001/ofr_01_50.djvu, 2001.

[10] Brasington, J., & Richards, K., *Turbidity and suspended sediment dynamics in small catchments in the Nepal Middle Hills.* Hydrol. Process. 14: 2559–2574, 2000.

[11] Campbell, G. S., *Soil Physics with Basic Transport Models for Soil-Plant Systems.* Developments in Soil Science 14, Elsevier New York, 1985

[12] De Sutter, R., Verhoeven, R., & Krein, A., *Simulation of sediment transport during flood events: laboratory work and field experiment.* Hydrol. Sc. 46(4): 599-610, 2001.

Relationships among basin area, sediment transport mechanisms and wood storage in mountain basins of the Dolomites (Italian Alps)

E. Rigon, F. Comiti, L. Mao & M. A. Lenzi
Department of Land and Agro-Forest Environments,
University of Padova, Legnaro, Padova, Italy

Abstract

The present work analyses the linkages between basin geology, shallow landslides, streambed morphology and debris flow occurrence in several small watersheds of the Dolomites (Italian Alps). Field survey and GIS analysis were carried out in order to seek correlations among basin area, basin geology, spatial frequency of landslides, in-channel wood storage, and local bed slope.

Keywords: large woody debris, landslides, bed morphology, Alps.

1 Introduction

Along with sediments, shallow landslides in forested basins supply channels with wood elements, which may have a strong impact on both channel morphology/stability and on debris flow dynamics.

Headwater channels, which make up 60–80% of the cumulative channel length in mountainous terrain [10, 11], are characterized by a strong coupling between hillslope and channel processes, in contrast to lowland streams. The switch between different transport mechanisms (e.g., bedload transport to debris flows) in the same channel often depends on the occurrence of shallow landslides feeding sediment in otherwise sediment-limited systems. Along with sediments, shallow landslides in forested basins supply channels with wood elements, which may have a strong impact on both channel morphology/stability

WIT Transactions on Engineering Sciences, Vol 60, © 2008 WIT Press
www.witpress.com, ISSN 1743-3533 (on-line)
doi:10.2495/DEB080171

and on debris flow dynamics. Large wood in the U.S Pacific Northwest and in Japan is long recognised to greatly influence the dynamics of debris flow channels, whereas poorly is known about its role in the European Alps.

Debris flows can transport large amount of wood [1, 6], which interact with the sediment-water mixture [4] and favour deposition. In steep headwater channels relative wood storage is higher than in lowland streams [2, 9] mostly because wood elements are very large compared to channel dimensions and thus are hardly transportable downstream by ordinary flows. Wood (along with sediment) tends to accumulate within these channels and only debris flow events can transport it substantially downstream and deposit it on alluvial fans and at confluences with higher-order tributaries [3, 7, 12].

The present work aims to evaluate wood load in mountain basins of varying size (1.2 to 70 km^2) of the Dolomites (Eastern Italian Alps) and to determine how wood input and transport processes change with basin scale.

2 Study sites and survey methods

2.1 Basin descriptions

The location of the 13 study basins is shown in Figure 2. The channels drain calcareous, sedimentary and igneous mountain catchments in the Southeastern Alps, within the administrative boundaries of the Province of Belluno, Italy.Table 1 reports a summary of the most important characteristics of the study basins. The location of the thirteen basins that are the subject of the present research is shown in fig. 1. Precipitation (1100 mm annual average) falls mainly in spring and autumn as cyclonic, long-duration rainfall, and as snowfall from December through April. Short-duration, intense summer rainstorms cause flash floods in the smaller basins (generally <2–3 km^2), where debris flow phenomena are very frequent. Sediment sources in the form of talus slopes, shallow landslides, bank erosion and slow mass movements are widespread but their abundance differs considerably according to the geology of each basin.

Forest cover (Table 1) of the basins – the upper tree limit is around 2000–2100 m a.s.l. – is mostly represented by conifers: spruce (*Picea abies*) within the elevation range 1000–1600 m a.s.l., whereas the upper zone (1600–2000 m a.s.l.) features mixed spruce-larch (*Larix decidua*) stands. No old-growth stands exist in the basins. In Italy as a whole, clear-cutting was banned at the beginning of last century to prevent soil erosion and increase soil retention capacity for flood attenuation. Only small areas (<100 m^2) are now logged contiguously. Nonetheless, the ruggedness of the terrain is such that most of the forested area is not harvested because it is unprofitable. Therefore, effects of logging slash on in-channel woody debris are expected to be small or negligible. Riparian vegetation is constituted by broadleaves at the lowest elevations (<1400–1500 m a.s.l.) – mostly alder (*Alnus incana*) with minor presence of ash (*Fraxinus excelsior*), maple (*Acer pseudoplatanus*), and willow (*Salix* spp) – and by spruce and larch in the upper part of the channels. Conifer trees typically have diameters on average around 0.3–0.4 m, whereas riparian broadleaves feature smaller sizes (<0.3 m).

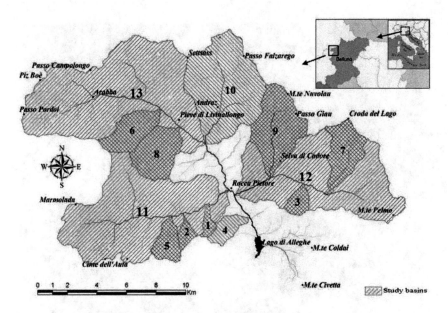

Figure 1:   Location map of the study basins (northeastern Italy). Numbers refer to Table 1.

Table 1:   General characteristic of the study basins.

Basin	Stream order	Area	Forested area	Mean elevation	Mean basin slope	Channel length	Mean channel slope	Dominant bed morphology
		(Km^2)	%	(m a.s.l.)	(%)	(Km)	(%)	
1- Bianco[a]	1	1,2	69	1724	72	2,2	38	cascade / bedrock
2- Miniere[a]	1	1,5	57	1886	75	1,9	28	falls / bedrock
3- Code[a]	2	2,2	89	1776	41	1,7	26	cascade/ bedrock
4- Molini	2	2,9	91	1609	51	3,6	16	step-pool / bedrock
5- Valbona	2	3,8	49	1888	76	3	21	cascade
6- Ornella	2	6,7	53	1961	54	4,6	18	cascade
7- Cordon	3	7,7	32	2075	47	5,5	10	step-pool
8- Davedino	2	8,7	48	1961	60	4	16	cascade
9- Codalunga	4	13,5	43	1930	55	6,4	10	cascade / step-pool
10- Andraz	4	27,2	44	1950	49	7,7	13	cascade / step-pool
11- Pettorina	4	51	41	1944	65	12,9	6	artificial / riffles [c]
12- Fiorentina	5[b]	58[b]	51	1838	55	12	4	artificial / riffles [c]
13- Cordevole	5	70	29	1194	51	13,3	3	artificial / riffles [c]

[a] Field evidences of debris flows.
[b] Actual drainage area at the downstream end section surveyed is 37 km^2 and stream order is 4.
[b] Sequences of concrete check-dams.

Figure 2:   Photos of the study channels: (a) Rio Bianco; (b) depositional reach in the Rio Code; (c) View of the Fiorentina; (d) debris flow fan deposited within the Cordevole (e) log step in the Rio Andraz; (f) wood-rich segment of the Rio Davedino.

2.2 Survey methodology

Field surveys were carried out from April 2004 to September 2007. Most streams were surveyed along the entire length of the main channel, whereas a systematic sampling scheme was adopted in some basins (Rio delle Miniere, Valbona, Ornella, Andraz and Rio Bianco), with 500-700 m-long segments were a-priori selected and which summed to 10% of the total channel length. Channel reaches were identified in the field based on uniformity of either slope, channel width, or abundance of wood. Bankfull width, depth and mean slope were measured in each reach. Bank erosions, landslides and tributary debris flow channels (fig. 2) were also recorded. All wood pieces >5 cm in diameter and >0.5 m in length lying within the active channel were measured by a tree calibre and tape meter respectively. Wood elements and wood jams were also classified as to their qualitative aspects [2, 8]. The volume of each log was calculated assuming a cylindrical shape, and wood storage for each reach was then derived as the total wood volume divided by channel area (i.e., bankfull width times reach length).

Basin area drained at each reach was calculated from a 5m x 5m Digital Elevation Model using GIS software.

3   Results

3.1 Channel width and slope as a function of drainage area

As expected, a positive correlation (based on log-transformed values, R=0.72, p<0.05) is observed between bankfull width (W) and drainage area (A) at the reach scale (Fig. 3). However, for A>20 km^2, a large scatter is present due to the

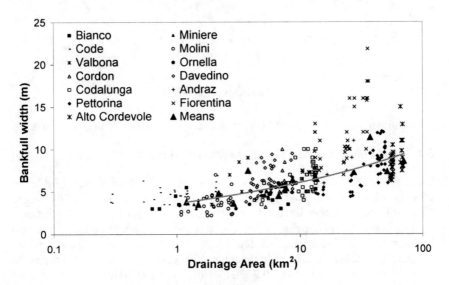

Figure 3:   Scatter plot of the bankfull width in relation to drainage area.

presence – in the Pettorina, Cordevole and Fiorentina rivers – of reaches whose cross-section was artificially widened when longitudinal and grade-control works were constructed. On the other hand, for $A < 1.5$ km^2, channel widths are fairly constant, around 5 m. This is likely due to the frequent occurrence of debris flows in the smaller basins analysed here [5].

The best-fit curve interpolating the average channel width for each basin (basin-scale analysis) is the following:

$$W = 3.82 \cdot A^{0.21} \qquad (1)$$

with $R^2 = 0.64$ (but $p > 0.05$).

As to mean channel slope (S), it turned out to be inversely correlated to drainage area (Fig. 4). The correlation – based on log-transformed data – is $R = -0.82$ ($p < 0.05$).

The regression curve calculated on basin-averaged slope values reads as:

$$S = 39.42 \cdot A^{-0.38} \qquad (2)$$

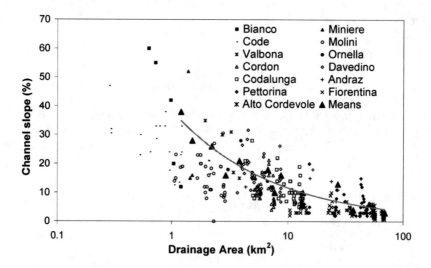

Figure 4: Scatter plot of the channel slope in relation to drainage area.

3.2 Wood dimensions and storage in the study basins

More than 9,000 wood elements were counted in the field survey (Table 2). Median log diameters (D_{50}) do not vary considerably among the study basins (0.08–0.13 m), whereas large differences exist with regard to log length (L_{50}= 0.79–3,75 m), but no correlation was found with basin size. In contrast, the ratio between the 84th percentile of log length and the average channel width (L_{84} Bkf^{-1}) remains close to 1 for channels < 3rd order ($A < 10$ km^2), and drops for higher-order basins (down to 0.2–0.3), with a correlation with basin area of $R = 0.68$ ($p < 0.1$). The ratio between the 84th percentile of log diameters and the average channel depth (D_{84} Dph^{-1}) it's always less than 0.5.

Table 2:   In-channel stored wood: quantity and sizes.

Basin	N° pieces	Vol wood	D_{16}	D_{50}	D_{84}	L_{16}	L_{50}	L_{84}	D_{84} Dph^{-1}	L_{84} Bkf^{-1}
		(m^3)	(m)	(m)	(m)	(m)	(m)	(m)		
Cordevole	775	52.4	0.06	0.09	0.17	0.8	1.7	3.8	0.27	0.44
Andraz	159	37.5	0.08	0.13	0.25	1.3	3.5	10.0	0.49	1.37
Bianco	77	9.3	0.06	0.11	0.23	0.7	1.2	3.7	0.49	0.96
Codalonga	818	42.9	0.05	0.07	0.14	1.0	2.9	6.4	0.26	0.98
Code	767	54.1	0.05	0.10	0.22	0.9	1.8	5.1	0.48	1.06
Cordon	602	44	0.05	0.11	0.18	1.2	2.1	5.8	0.25	1.07
Davedino	2013	191.1	0.07	0.12	0.22	0.9	2.0	5.0	0.32	0.78
Miniere	184	6.86	0.06	0.10	0.20	0.6	1.2	3.2	0.46	0.91
Fiorentina	1557	97.53	0.05	0.10	0.19	1.0	1.7	3.9	0.33	0.34
Molini	655	40.04	0.06	0.10	0.20	0.8	1.6	4.0	0.42	1.11
Ornella	119	4.42	0.05	0.07	0.12	1.0	1.7	3.9	0.26	0.87
Pettorina	1320	50.76	0.05	0.08	0.14	0.4	0.8	1.6	0.25	0.22
Valbona	44	4.4	0.05	0.11	0.18	0.9	2.8	5.1	0.46	0.68

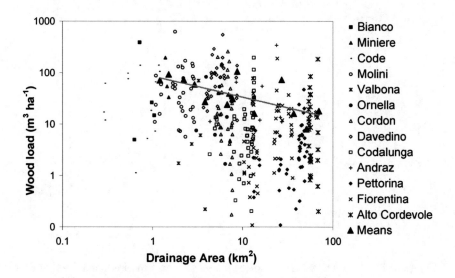

Figure 5:   Scatter plot of the in-channel volume of stored wood (in relation with the surface channel) and the drainage area.

Therefore, a much higher mobility of wood elements might be envisaged for such channels [9], and this could be a reason for their lower wood load per unit of bed area (V_w, Fig. 5). However, these larger basins present also higher degrees of human impact (roads, towns, control works) which are presumed to contribute to diminish the presence of in-channel wood. On the other hand, extremely high wood loads (>70 m^{3}ha^{-1}) can be found in relatively large catchments too, as the case of the Andraz creek ($A=27.2$ km^2). However, because this stream was surveyed using the partial sampling procedure (see above), this indication must be regarded with caution. The best-fit regression curve on basin-averaged wood loads is as follows:

$$V_w = 84.92 \cdot A^{-0.31} \tag{3}$$

The relationship features a very low R^2 (0.33) and is significant only at $p<0.10$. Two basins (Andraz and Davedino) appear to lower the correlation with drainage area, plotting well above the power trend curve. Indeed, Fig. 5 shows a very large scatter of the reach-based wood loads ($R=-0.39$, $p<0.05$).

3.3 Hillslope instabilities and wood storage

The scatter is Fig. 5 indicates that several factors other than basin/channel size affect wood load. During the field surveys became evident that reaches storing high wood volumes were associated to the presence of landslides or debris flow tributaries (fig. 2b,2d,2f) which supply streams with large conifer trees.

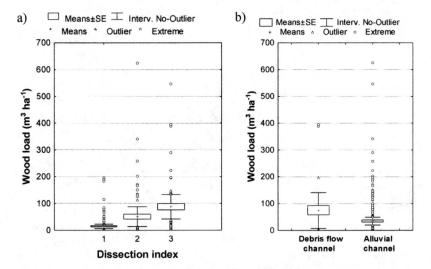

Figure 6:   Box and whisker plot of the variation in the in-channel volume of stored wood in relation to a) dissection index: 1= low 2= medium 3= higth b) Debris flow-prone channels.

During the survey, each reach was given a score reflecting – along its banks – the linear extension of landslides, bank erosions, and/or the confluence with debris flow channels. In order to calculate a "dissection index" (DI) at the basin scale, reach-scale values were averaged weighted on reach length, and each basin was then assigned to one of three classes (1–3) with increasing degrees of dissection. Figure 6a shows that wood load on average increases with DI. Looking instead at differences in wood load between debris flow and alluvial channels (Fig. 6b), these are less clear to due to high number of outliers present in the latter. A two-way ANOVA including as factors the dissection index and the channel type (debris flow vs. alluvial) was carried out. Results confirms the statistical relevance of DI (Fig. 7a, $p<0.01$) whereas the difference between channel types (Fig. 7b) is not significant ($p>0.10$). However, debris flow channels (Miniere, Bianco, Code) seem to present smaller wood loading. It is important to mention that basin-averaged DI is correlated negatively with drainage area ($R=-0,66$, $p<0.05$) and positively with channel slope ($R=0.57$, $p<0.05$).

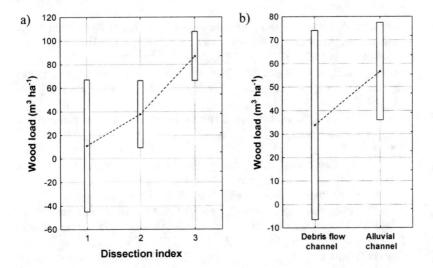

Figure 7:   Variance analysis. The vertical box indicating confidence intervals to 95% a) dissection index b) Debris flow-prone channels.

4   Conclusions

High wood loading in mountain channels of the Dolomites tend to be more frequent in low order ($<3^{rd}$, $A<10$ km^2) channels, but appears to be strongly associated to the degree of basin instability encompassing landslides and debris flows tributaries. However, wood mobility in these narrow streams is very limited and is likely to become substantial only with infrequently large flood events, or when debris flows occur in the channels. Wood transfer is potentially more efficient for higher order streams, thus leading to a higher frequency of wood-related hazards (e.g., bridge obstructions). Therefore, to reduce flood hazards associated to excessive wood transport, priority should be given to: i) prevent large mass wasting in forested areas; ii) design bridges taking into account wood transport; and, only if economically worth, iii) build trapping structures in debris flow channels entering directly large (order >4) streams and/or in these large channels upstream of sensitive locations (towns, bridges).

References

[1] Bigelow, P.E., Benda, L.E., Miller, D.J. and Burnett, K.M. On Debris Flows, River Networks, and the Spatial Structure of Channel Morphology *Forest Science 53(2)* 220–238, 2007.

[2] Comiti F., Andreoli A., Lenzi M.A., and Mao L. Spatial density and characteristics of woody debris in five mountain rivers of the Dolomites (Italian Alps). *Geomorphology 78, Issues 1-2,* 44–63, 2006.

[3] Dietrich W.E., Dunne, T. Sediment budget for a small catchment in mountainous terrain. *Zeitschrift fur Geomorphologie N.F. 29*:191–206, 1978.

[4] Lancaster, S.T., Hayes, S.K. and Grant, G.E. Effects of wood on debris flow runout in small mountain watersheds. *Water Resour. Res. 39(6)*: 1168doi: 10.1029/2001WR001227, 2003.

[5] Leopold, L.B., and Maddock, T. Jr., The hydraulic geometry of stream channels and some physiographic implications, *U.S. Geol. Surv. Prof. Pap.,* 252, 1953.

[6] May, C.L. Debris flows through different forest age classes in the central Oregon Coast Range, *J. Am. Wat. Resourc. Assoc., 38(4),* 1097–1113, 2002.

[7] May, C.L., Gresswell, R.E. Process and rates of sediment and wood accumulation in headwater streams of the Oregon Coast Range, USA. *Earth Surface Processes and Landforms 28,* 409–424, 2003

[8] Rigon E., Andreoli A., Comiti F., Lenzi M.A. Quantity, characteristic and origin of large woody debris in a mountain stream (Codalunga, Veneto). *Quaderni di Idronomia Montana 25,* 227–243, 2007

[9] Rigon E., Comiti F., Andreoli A., Lenzi M.A. Wood in mountain streams of the Alps: too much or too little? Evidences from the upper Cordevole basin (Belluno) *Quaderni di Idronomia Montana* accepted.

[10] Schumm, S.A. Evolution of drainage systems and slopes in badlands at Perth Amboy, New Jersey. *Bulletin of the Geological Society of America* 67: 597–646, 1956.

[11] Shreve, R.L. Stream lengths and basin areas in topologically random channel networks. *Journal of Geology 77*: 397–414, 1969.

[12] Swanson F.J., Fredricksen, R.L., McCorison, F.M. Material transfer in a western Oregon forested watershed. In *Analysis of Coniferous Forest Ecosystems in the Western United States,* Edmonds RL (ed.). Hutchinson Ross: New York; 233–266, 1982.

Large wood and flash floods: evidence from the 2007 event in the Davča basin (Slovenia)

F. Comiti[1], L. Mao[1,3], E. Preciso[2], L. Picco[1],
L. Marchi[2] & M. Borga[1]
[1]*Department of Land and Agroforest Environment,*
University of Padova, Italy
[2]*CNR – IRPI, Padova, Italy*
[3]*Department of Geography, University of Hull, UK*

Abstract

This paper presents the evidence gathered during a post-flood survey in a Slovenian mountain basin (Davča basin, drainage area of 32 km^2) following the catastrophic flood of September 2007. Channel avulsion, debris flows and landslides delivered large volumes of wood into the channel, and massive wood accumulations were found at the basin outlet. Wood-induced dam-break flows were therefore hypothesised to be responsible for most of the damages. Field observations and approximate discharge estimations indicate that the damages suffered in the Davča basin can be attributed to excessive wood load only to a limited extent, and that the critical factors were narrow road crossings which acted as traps for sediment and wood.

Keywords: woody debris, flash floods, mountain rivers, Slovenia.

1   Flood hazards due to natural dams and large wood

Mountain valleys are subject to several natural hazards, which include mass wasting, debris flow and fluvial processes. However, some of the most hazardous phenomena occur when the three phenomena interact, as in the case of temporary damming of stream channels by landslides [6, 7, 12] or debris-flow deposits which often include large wood (LW) [1, 8, 10]. In fact, the subsequent breaching and collapse of these dams release destructive dam-break waves which can attain extremely high flow discharges, unpredictable from a mere hydrological perspective [9]. As a consequence, such events are thought to

WIT Transactions on Engineering Sciences, Vol 60, © 2008 WIT Press
www.witpress.com, ISSN 1743-3533 (on-line)
doi:10.2495/DEB080181

represent the most effective and dramatic geomorphic phenomena in mountain channels [5]. Indeed, natural dam-break processes – transporting huge amounts of wood (Fig. 1) – have caused some of the largest damages in several valleys of the Dolomites (Italian Alps) during the 1966 catastrophic flooding [3, 4]. The extreme magnitude of floods caused by the failure of natural dams is matched by a typically low frequency (>50–100 yr), such that these events may be easily forgotten, thus allowing unwise human occupation of flood-prone corridors. This paper presents a qualitative analysis of the geomorphic processes triggered by an intense flash flood occurred in a mountain basin of the Slovenian Alps, which featured considerable LW transport and deposition. The underlying hypothesis is that the extreme water stages observed and the damages could be ascribed – at least partially – to the collapse of temporary dams formed by sediments and LW.

Figure 1:   Huge volumes of wood were transported along the Fiorentina river and invaded the small town of Caprile (Italian Alps) during the 1966 flood (R.I. >100 yr).

2   The flash flood of September 2007 in Slovenia

On 18th September 2007, there was widespread flash flooding in Slovenia. The flooding caused seven casualties and about €300 million of damages. The precipitation featured a convective bands structure and extremely large rainfall gradients. The consequence of such precipitation pattern was that nearby small basins responded in sharply different ways. The storm lasted for 10-14 hours, depending on locations. The cumulated precipitation ranged in most basins between 250 to 300 mm. The storm led to a distributed flash flooding along the Sava and Selščica Sora rivers [2, 11].

3   Study area and methods

The study area is the Davča basin (32 km^2, Fig. 2), one of the tributaries of the Selščica Sora river most severely hit by the flash flood (230 mm of cumulated

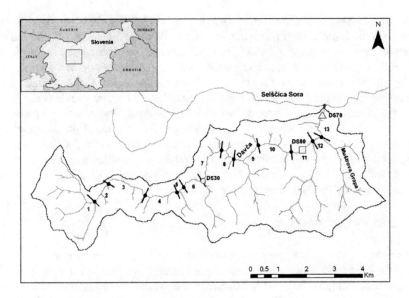

Figure 2:   The Davča catchment with channel subdivision into 13 reaches and the cross-sections where peak discharge was estimated. The location map in the upper left corner shows the area affected by the flood of September 2007 in the Sora River basin.

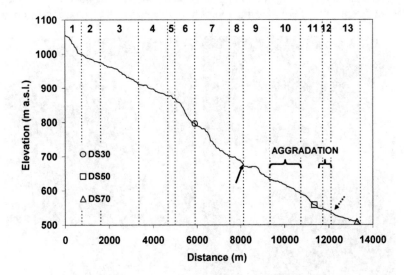

Figure 3:   Longitudinal profile of the Davča Torrent. The solid row indicates the location of a major debris flow tributary, and the dotted line arrow the confluence with the Muštrova Grapa. The void symbols (circle, square, triangle) locate cross-sections where discharge was estimated (see also Fig. 2).

rainfall, estimated recurrence interval about 250 yr [2]). The Davča main channel was separated into different reaches in order to describe the processes related to sediment and to large wood (LW) source, transport and deposition which took place during the flood event. The reaches are marked on the longitudinal profile (Fig. 3), which was derived from the DEM of the basin (12.5 m grid size), and therefore can be used for describing the channel bed at a large scale (i.e. > 100 m) only. Peak discharges were estimated from the flood marks, surveying with a total station 3 cross sections (2 in the Davča Torrent and 1 in its tributary Mustrova Grapa). For each cross section, the longitudinal bed slope and the highest flood marks were surveyed, and roughness coefficient was estimated based on grain size and channel morphology. The peak discharge was then calculated using the Manning-Strickler equation.

4 Field observations

Evidence of intense sediment transport were found at the headwaters (reach 1) below a 15-m high waterfall, and on a right tributary between the reaches 1 and 2 (hyper-concentrated flow with abundant LW recruited from the hillslopes). Overall, deposition of sediment and LW characterized the entire reach 2. Wood from upstream was trapped by the valley floor forest and by trees fallen into the channel as a consequence of bank erosion. The wide reach 2 ends at a road crossing where an eyewitness reported that the small bridge did not experience clogging during the flood, indicating how sediment and wood transport rates were not "excessive" here, despite a very high discharge (the flood marks are at

Figure 4:   Steep tributaries incised to bedrock and recruited many LW elements which were too long to be transferred to the main channel.

an elevation 2.5–3 times the bankfull stage) was already present in this upper part of the basin. Also in the next downstream reaches (3 and 4), the event did not cause major instabilities in the channel. As a consequence, these two reaches lack significant wood and sediment sources adjacent to channel. Furthermore, several steep right-hand tributaries surely experienced high flow rates, but sediments and LW delivered to the main channel were of minor influence. Most of them underwent incision (up to 1 m) reaching the bedrock, with widespread bank erosion and associated recruitment of large trees, which could not be transported to the Davča (Fig. 4).

However, a road crossing (probably under-sized) between the reaches 4 and 5 likely caused backwater effects which led the channel to shift towards a forested floodplain just upstream of the bridge. Here many trees were recruited, further obstructing the bridge. In fact, there is evidence (lateral depositions, wood jams, Fig. 5(a)) that the main channel here spilled over the bridge. Downstream of it (reach 5), several huge LW jams (mostly composed of "fresh" trees) were trapped by standing trees on the floodplain and channel bends (Fig. 5(b)).

(a)   (b)

Figure 5:   The effect of the bridge between reaches 4-5: (a) deposition and floodplain erosion upstream of the bridge; (b) high wood accumulations downstream of the bridge.

These jams are up to 2m high, thus testifying a very high stage for a wide (15–20 m) cross-section. A possible flow surge issued from the bridge may be envisaged, but its effect must have been limited in length due to its small height and stored volume. Downstream of a check-dam (which separates reaches 5 and 6), the channel becomes steeper and then flows within a gorge over large boulders. Several large trees (beeches and spruces) fallen from the adjacent slopes are also present, but their transport was prevented by the narrow channel width. Between the reaches 6 and 7, the slope is lower, and the confinement of the channel on the right bank is less strict. Here the peak discharge was estimated to about 55 m^3s^{-1} (DS30 in Figs. 2–3, drainage area 9.8 km^2, 5.6 $m^3s^{-1}km^{-2}$).

Reach 7 is morphologically comparable to reach 6 and features a small debris flow on a right-hand tributary. In the reach 8, the main channel presents a milder slope and the valley floor widens considerably, with the presence of a grassy floodplain. A probable hyper-concentrated flow on a left-hand tributary delivered some sediment to Davča. In contrast, the next channel reach (9), flowing in a gorge, features relatively abundant sediment sources from the right bank (debris flows, landslides).

The reach ends at a bridge which was clogged by a probable combination of high water stage, intense coarse sediment transport, and floating LW supplied by nearby debris flows. Bridge clogging is indicated by upstream deposition of wood and sediment (Fig. 6). The backwater effect led to channel aggradation, forcing the stream to flow on the road.

(a)　　　　　　　　　　　　　　　　　　　　　　　　(b)

Figure 6:　The bridge between reaches 9-10: (a) from downstream right after the flood; (b) from upstream two months later. Source for a: *http://www.davca.si*. The arrow indicates the flood marks.

Figure 7:　The narrow reach 11, featuring bank and bed erosion. Source: *http://www.davca.si*.

The road embankment and the bridge obstruction finally breached, probably causing a flow surge downstream where high-elevation (>2 m) marks were observed at channel banks. Reach 10 displays deposition of coarse sediment (up to 0.8-1 m in diameter) and further sediment inputs from the left slope (a small debris flow channel and several small landslides). Intense channel aggradation occurred where the valley widens, upstream of a bridge which collapsed and a huge LW jam was trapped upstream.

The steeper, narrower reach downstream (11, Fig. 7) was characterized by diffuse bank erosion and local bed incision. Peak discharge here (drainage area 21.4 km^2) was estimated around 150 m^{3}s^{-1} (i.e., 7 m^{3}s^{-1}km^{-2}, DS50 in Figs. 2–3).

Downstream, the Davča receives two important right-hand tributaries (Farji Potok and Muštrova Grapa), which did not show evidence of major channel changes and sediment transport, their bed still showing stable step-pool sequences. The peak discharge on the Muštrova Grapa just upstream of the confluence with the Davča (drainage area 4.2 km^2) was evaluated to be 13 m^{3}s^{-1} (3.1 m^{3}s^{-1} km^{-2}). Although lower than those observed in the upper Davča basin, these values indicate a high-magnitude flood. The bed stability of Farji Potok and Muštrova Grapa may be ascribed to a coarser surface layer and to a more developed bed structuring compared to the upper Davča.

Just upstream of the confluence with the Muštrova Grapa (reach 12), in correspondence of a widening of the valley floor, the Davča aggraded considerably; bridges were buried with sediments and wood and the flow invaded the road at left side (Fig. 8).

The bridge at the Muštrova-Davča confluence trapped some LW, but did not collapse because most of the floodwater was flowing on the road (Fig. 9). Part of the floating LW was then trapped by some trees at the road junction, while some accumulated against a building which was heavily damaged.

Figure 8: Channel aggradation and channel avulsion along reach 12, with a bridge clogged by LW. Source: www.davca.si.

Very coarse clasts (up to 0.8–1 m in diameter) were deposited upstream of the trees, and LW jams were up to 2 m high, both indicating very high stream power values. The total LW volume was estimated around 80 m^3, but much had been already carried away during restoration works. The longest wood elements (up to 8 m, roughly corresponding to channel width at the near upstream reaches) appeared to derive from riparian trees eroded by the flood, and the integrity of

Figure 9:   The Davča at the confluence with the Muštrova Grapa: (a) the bridge – not collapsed – from downstream right after the flood; (b) the LW jams trapped at the junction (November 2007). The arrow indicates the bridge location. Source for a: *http://www.davca.si.*

the bark cover hints to a brief transport distance, possibly just a reach length. In contrast, many shorter pieces showed clear signs of long residence time within the channel.

Only a minor volume of LW elements likely reached the channel downstream of the confluence with the Muštrova Grapa) and could be transported downstream (reach 13) towards the Selščica Sora. It is interesting to note that the peak discharge estimated for the Davča just upstream of the confluence with the Sora is less (120 m^{3}s^{-1}, 3.8 m^{3}s^{-1} km^{-2}, DS70) than at the upstream cross-section DS50. Bearing in mind the large degree of uncertainty intrinsic in the flow peak estimates, their interpretation suggests either flood attenuation in the lower part of the stream (e.g., due to valley widening downstream of section DS50), a dam-break flow surge related to the obstructed bridge between reaches 9-10, or their combination.

5   Conclusions

Field observations have shown that large amounts of sediment and LW were mobilised within the basin, with a large variability of the intensity of supply processes. However, although a quantitative assessment of sediment and LW discharged by the Davča Torrent to the Sora River was not possible, the amount of sediment deposited on the floodplain at the confluence between these two streams appears to be small in comparison to sediment transport and LW mobilisation observed within the drainage basin. The short duration of the highest discharges, reported by local witnesses, probably contributed to limit the distances of transport, thus reducing sediment delivery to the outlet of the catchment. The post-flood survey gave evidence that transfer of large wood elements from the headwaters to the main channel was mostly associated to debris flows. In contrast, fluvial processes in small, low-order streams are not able to transport long, newly-recruited logs which remain stored in such channels. Other important wood sources were represented by forested floodplains in reaches where aggradation led to channel avulsion.

In conclusion, with regard to the considerable damages suffered in the Davča basin, they can be attributed to the combination of: i) very intense, infrequent precipitation; ii) locally large sediment and LW inputs, mostly from debris flows; iii) presence of critical narrow sections (road crossing); and, most importantly, iv) human occupation of valley areas naturally prone to flooding and channel aggradation.

Acknowledgements

This study was funded by the European Union's Sixth Framework Programme through the STREP Project *HYDRATE*, Contract GOCE 037024. The authors are grateful to the Environmental Agency of the Republic of Slovenia (ARSO) for providing the DEM of the studied basin and for the collaboration in field observations and in the interviews to eyewitnesses of the flood.

References

[1]   Andreoli A., Comiti F. & Lenzi M.A., Characteristic, distribution and geomorphic role of large woody debris in a mountain stream of the Chilean Andes. *Earth Surface Processes and Landforms*, 33(11), 1675–1692, 2007.

[2]   ARSO (Agencija Republike Slovenije za Okolje), Poročilo o vremenski in hidrološki situaciji 18 septembra 2007. *Governmental Report*, www.arso.gov.si, 2007.

[3]   Castiglioni, G.B., Note di commento alla carta dell'alluvione del novembre 1966 nel Veneto e nel Trentino-Alto Adige: effetti morfologici e allagamenti. In: Castiglioni G.B. (Ed.) *Le calamità naturali nelle Alpi*, Proc. XXI Congresso Geografico Italiano, Verbania, Vol 2(1), 269–290. 1974.

[4]   Comiti F., Andreoli A., Lenzi M.A. & Mao L., Spatial density and characteristics of woody debris in five mountain rivers of the Dolomites (Italian Alps). *Geomorphology* 78, 44–63, 2006.

[5]   Costa J.E., Schuster R.L., The formation and failure of natural dams. *Geological Society of America Bulletin* 100, 1054–1068, 1988.

[6]   Davies T.R., Scott B.J., Landslide dam-break flood hazard from the Callery Gorge, South Westland, New Zealand. *Journal of Hydrology* (NZ) 36(1), 1–13, 1997.

[7]   Hancox G., McSaveney M.J., Manville V.R., Davies T.R., The October 1999 Mt Adams rock avalanche and subsequent landslide dam-break flood and effects in Poerua River, Westland, New Zealand. *New Zealand Journal of Geology & Geophysics* 48, 683–705, 2005.

[8]   Ishikawa, Y., Studies on disaster caused by debris flow carrying floating logs down mountain streams. SABO Department, Public Works Research Institute, Tsukuba, Japan, 1990.

[9]   Jakob M., Jordan P., Design flood estimates in mountain streams – the need for a geomorphic approach. *Can. J. Civ. Eng.,* 28(3), 425–439, 2001.

[10] Lancaster S.T., Hayes S.K., Grant G.E., The effects of wood on debris flow runout in small mountainous watersheds. *Water Resources Research* 39(6):1168, doi:10.1029/2001WR001227

[11] Marchi L., Bain V., Intensive post-event campaign in the Selščica Sora river basin, Slovenia, after the flash flood of September 18, 2007. *Hydrate Project IPEC Report*, pp. 44, 2007.

[12] Marchi, L., Cavalli, M., Procedures for the Documentation of Historical Debris Flows: Application to the Chieppena Torrent (Italian Alps). *Environmental Management*, 40, 493–503, 2007.

Dam-break shock waves: a two-phase model for mature and immature debris flow

D. De Wrachien[1] & S. Mambretti[2]

[1]Department of Agricoltural Hydraulics, State University of Milan, Italy
[2]DIIAR, Politecnico di Milano, Italy

Abstract

To predict flood and debris flow dynamics a numerical model, based on 1D De Saint Venant (SV) equations, modified for including erosion/deposition processes along the path, was developed. The McCormack–Jameson shock capturing scheme was employed for the solution of the equations, written in a conservative law form. This technique was applied to determine both the propagation and the profile of a two-phase debris flow resulting from the instantaneous and complete collapse of a storage dam. To validate the model, comparisons have been made between its predictions and laboratory tests concerning flows of water and homogeneous granular mixtures in a uniform geometry flume reproducing dam-break waves. Agreements between computational and experimental results are considered very satisfactory for mature (non-stratified) debris flows, which embrace most real cases. To better predict immature (stratified) flows, the model was improved in order to feature, in a more realistic way, the distribution of the particles of different size within the mixture. The level of maturity of the flow is assessed by an empirical, yet experimental based, criterion. The model, at this stage, should be able to predict the whole debris flow phenomenon, i.e. the triggering, mobilising and stopping processes of both mature and immature debris flows in different dam-break conditions. On the whole, the model proposed can easily be extended to channels with arbitrary cross sections for debris flow routing, as well as for solving problems of unsteady flow in open channels by incorporating the appropriate initial and boundary conditions. The model could also be improved to predict and assess the propagation and stoppage processes of debris and hyper-concentrated flows in mountainous catchments and river basins, triggered by extreme hydrological events, once validated on the basis of field data.

Keywords: debris flow, dam-break, two-phase modelling, mature and immature mixtures.

WIT Transactions on Engineering Sciences, Vol 60, © 2008 WIT Press
www.witpress.com, ISSN 1743-3533 (on-line)
doi:10.2495/DEB080191

1 Introduction

In this paper a 1D two-phase model for debris flow propagation is proposed. SV equations, modified for including erosion / deposition processes along the mixture path, are used for expressing conservation of mass and momentum for the two phases of the mixture. The scheme is validated for dam-break problems comparing numerical results with experimental data. Comparisons are made between both wave depths and front propagation velocities obtained respectively on the basis of laboratory tests and with predictions from the numerical model proposed by McCormack [18] and Jameson [13].

In order to analyze stratified (immature) flow – the solid/liquid mixture is present in the lower layer, while only water is present in the upper one – the model has been improved by taking into account mass and momentum conservation equations for each phase and layer. Momentum conservation equations describe energy exchanges between the two phases in the same layer and between layers, while mass conservation equations describe mass exchange layers [16, 17].

2 Theoretical approach

Debris flow resulting from flash floods such as a sudden collapse of a dam (dam-break) are often characterised by the formation of shock waves caused by many factors such as valley contractions, irregular bed slope and non-zero tailwater depth. It is commonly accepted that a mathematical description of these phenomena can be accomplished by means of 1D SV equations [2, 4, 5].

Numerical treatments of such equations, generally, require schemes capable of preserving discontinuities, possibly without any special shift (shock-capturing schemes). Most numerical approaches have been developed in the last two or three decades, that include the use of finite differences, finite elements or discrete/distinct element methods [1, 19].

2.1 Governing equations

The 1D approach for unsteady debris flow triggered by dam-break is governed by the SV equations. This set of partial differential equations describes a system of hyperbolic conservation laws with source term (S) and can be written in compact vector form:

$$\frac{\partial \mathbf{V}}{\partial t} + \frac{\partial \mathbf{F}}{\partial s} = \mathbf{S} \tag{1}$$

where:

$$\mathbf{V} = \begin{pmatrix} A \\ Q \end{pmatrix} \qquad \mathbf{F} = \begin{pmatrix} Q \\ \dfrac{Q^2}{A} + g \cdot I_1 \end{pmatrix} \qquad \mathbf{S} = \begin{pmatrix} 0 \\ g \cdot A \cdot (i - S_i) + g \cdot I_2 \end{pmatrix}$$

with $A(s,t)$: wetted cross-sectional area; $Q(s,t)$: flow rate; s: spatial coordinate; t: temporal coordinate; g: acceleration due to gravity; i: bed slope; S_i: bed resistance term or friction slope, that can be modelled using different rheological laws [19].

The pressure force integrals I_1 and I_2 are calculated in accordance with the geometrical properties of the channel. I_1 represents a hydrostatic pressure form term and I_2 represents the pressure forces due to the longitudinal width variation, expressed as:

$$I_1 = \int_0^h (H-\eta)\sigma(s,\eta)\cdot d\eta \quad I_2 = \int_0^h (H-\eta)\cdot \frac{\partial\sigma}{\partial s}\cdot d\eta \quad (2)$$

where H: water depth; η: integration variable indicating distance from the channel bottom; $\sigma(s,\eta)$: channel width at distance η from the channel bed, expressed as:

$$\sigma(s,\eta) = \frac{\partial A(s,\eta)}{\partial \eta} \quad (3)$$

To take into account erosion/deposition processes along the debris flow propagation path, which are directly related to both the variation of the mixture density and the temporal evolution of the channel bed, a mass conservation equation for the solid phase and a erosion/deposition model have been introduced in the SV approach. Defining the sediment discharge as:

$$q(s,t) = E \cdot B \quad (4)$$

with E: erosion/deposition rate; B: wetted bed width, the modified vector form of the SV equations can be expressed as follows:

$$\frac{\partial \mathbf{V}}{\partial t} + \frac{\partial \mathbf{F}}{\partial s} = \mathbf{S} \quad (5)$$

where:

$$\mathbf{V} = \begin{pmatrix} A \\ Q \\ c_s \cdot A \end{pmatrix} \quad \mathbf{F} = \begin{pmatrix} Q \\ \dfrac{Q^2}{A} + g \cdot I_1 \\ c_s \cdot Q \end{pmatrix} \quad \mathbf{S} = \begin{pmatrix} q(s,t) \\ g \cdot A(i - S_i) + g \cdot I_2 \\ E \cdot c_* \cdot B \end{pmatrix}$$

with c_s: volumetric solid concentration in the mixture; c^*: bed volumetric solid concentration.

2.2 Two phase mathematical model

In the present work granular and liquid phases are considered. The model includes two mass and momentum balance equations for both the liquid and solid phases respectively. The interaction between phases is simulated according to the Wan and Wang [21] hypothesis. The system is completed with equations to estimate erosion / deposition rate derived from the Egashira and Ashida [7] relationship and by the assumption of the Mohr and Coulomb failure criterion for non cohesive materials.

2.2.1 Mass and momentum equations for the liquid phase

Mass and momentum equations for water can be expressed in conservative form as:

$$\frac{\partial Q_l(s,t)}{\partial s} + \frac{\partial(c_l \cdot A(s,t))}{\partial t} = 0 \tag{6}$$

$$\frac{\partial Q_l}{\partial t} + \frac{\partial}{\partial s}\left(\beta \cdot \frac{Q_l^2}{c_l \cdot A}\right) = g \cdot c_l \cdot A \cdot \left(i - J - \frac{\partial H}{\partial s}\right) - F \tag{7}$$

with $Q_l(s,t)$: flow discharge; c_l: volumetric concentration of water in the mixture; β: momentum correction coefficient that we will assume to take the value $\beta = 1$ from now on; J: slope of the energy line according to Chézy's formula; i: bed slope; F: friction force between the two phases.

According to Wan and Wang [21], the interaction of the phases at single granule level f is given by:

$$f = c_D \cdot \frac{\pi \cdot d_{50}^2}{4} \cdot \frac{\rho_l \cdot (v_l - v_s)}{2} \cdot |v_l - v_s| \tag{8}$$

with c_D: drag coefficient; v_l: velocity of water; v_s: velocity of the solid phase; d_{50}: mean diameter of the coarse particle; ρ_l: liquid density.

Assuming grains of spherical shape and defining the control volume of the mixture as:

$$V_c = B \cdot H \cdot \cos\vartheta \cdot ds \approx B \cdot H \cdot ds \tag{9}$$

with ϑ channel slope angle, which holds for low channel slopes, the whole friction force F between the two phases for the control volume can be written as:

$$F = \frac{3}{4} \cdot c_D \cdot \rho_l \cdot (v_l - v_s) \cdot |v_l - v_s| \cdot \frac{c_s}{d_{50}} \cdot H \cdot B \cdot ds \tag{10}$$

2.2.2 Mass and momentum equations for the solid phase

Mass and momentum conservation equations for the solid phase of the mixture can be expressed as:

$$\frac{\partial(c_s \cdot A)}{\partial t} + \frac{\partial Q_s}{\partial s} = E \cdot c_* \cdot B \tag{11}$$

$$\frac{\partial Q_s}{\partial t} + \frac{\partial}{\partial s}\left(\beta \cdot \frac{Q_s^2}{c_s \cdot A}\right) = -g \cdot \frac{\rho_s - \rho_l}{\rho_s} \cdot c_s \cdot (1 + i^2) \cdot \frac{\partial H}{\partial s} \cdot A + F +$$

$$+ g \cdot \frac{\rho_s - \rho_l}{\rho_s} \cdot c_s \cdot (i^2 - 1) \cdot tg\delta \cdot A + g \cdot \frac{\rho_s - \rho_l}{\rho_s} \cdot c_s \cdot A \cdot i \tag{12}$$

with $Q_s(s,t)$: discharge of the solid rate; ρ_s: solid phase density.

According to Ghilardi et at. [10] and to Egashira and Ashida [7], the bed volumetric solid concentration c_* was assumed to be constant and the erosion velocity rate E a function of the mixture velocity U:

$$E = U \cdot k_E \cdot tg(\vartheta_f - \vartheta_e) \tag{13}$$

with k_E: coefficient equal to 0.1 according to experimental data [7, 10–12].

Positive or negative values of E correspond to granular material erosion or deposition, respectively.

ϑ_f and ϑ_e represent the energy line and the bed equilibrium angles, respectively, expressed as [6]:

$$\vartheta_f = arctg\left[\frac{J}{\cos\vartheta}\right] \tag{14}$$

$$\vartheta_e = arctg\left[\frac{c_s \cdot (\rho_s - \rho)}{c_s \cdot (\rho_s - \rho) + \rho} \cdot tg\phi\right] \tag{15}$$

where the debris flow density is defined as:

$$\rho = (\rho_s - \rho_l) \cdot c_s + \rho_l \tag{16}$$

and ϕ is the static internal friction angle. U is defined as follows:

$$U = c_s v_s + c_l v_l \tag{17}$$

For J the Takahashi [20] equation has been chosen, according to the dilatant fluid hypothesis developed by Bagnold [3]:

$$J = S_i = \frac{U^2}{\left(\frac{2}{5 \cdot d_{50}} \cdot \frac{H}{\lambda}\right)^2 \cdot \frac{1}{a_b \cdot sen\, \delta} \cdot \left[c_s + (1 - c_s) \cdot \frac{\rho_l}{\rho_s}\right] \cdot g \cdot R} \tag{18}$$

with S_i: friction term and R: hydraulic radius given by:

$$R = \frac{A}{P} \tag{19}$$

where P is the wetted perimeter.

The quantity λ (linear concentration) depends on the granulometry of the solids in the form:

$$\lambda = \frac{c_s^{1/3}}{c_m^{1/3} - c_s^{1/3}} \tag{20}$$

where c_m: maximum packing volume fraction (for perfect spheres $c_m = 0.74$); a_b: empirical constant.

With regard to the momentum conservation equation (12) all its terms have been evaluated considering only the fraction of volume actually occupied by grains and ignoring the erosion/deposition velocity.

3 Experimental results and model calibration

To validate the model, comparisons have been made between its predictions and experimental results carried out in the Hydraulic Laboratory of the Politecnico di Milano. Numerical solutions of the SV equations are based on the well-known

McCormack–Jameson predictor-corrector finite difference scheme ([13, 18]). The tests were performed with flows of water and homogeneous granular mixtures in a uniform geometry flume reproducing dam-break waves ([14, 15]). The experimental set-up consisted of a loading tank (dimensions 0.5 m x 0.5 m x 0.9 m) with a downstream wall made of sluice gate, a pneumatic control device and a very short opening time (0.3 s).

The mixture flowed in a 6 m long channel of square section (0.5 m x 0.5 m) and adjustable slope. To enable camera recordings, one of the flume lateral walls contained glass windows.

Experimental tests were performed by changing the channel slope, the bottom roughness (smooth bottom made of galvanised plate or rough bottom covered with an homogeneous layer of gravel, with d_{50} = 0.005 m), the solid material characteristics (vedril: $\rho = 1168\ kg/m^3$, d_{50} = 0.003 m; or gravel: $\rho = 2621\ kg/m^3$ d_{50} = 0.005 m) and the volumetric concentration of the mixture.

Recordings were made with a Sony Digital Handcam, model DCR-TRV32 E camera, which had an acquisition velocity of 25 frames per second, and were electronically elaborated.

To take into account different behaviours of the flow, the experimental data have been compared with the predictions of three rheological laws included in the one phase model (called "Water", "Fix Bagnold" and "Mobile Bagnold") and with those of the two phase model.

Comparisons show good agreement on the general shape that includes a steep front immediately followed by the maximum wave height and a decrease in flow depths down to an asymptotic value reached at the stoppage (figures 1 and 2).

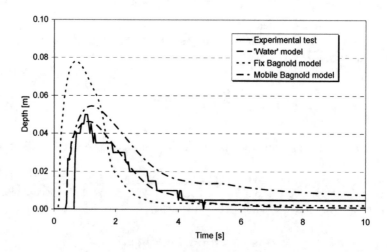

Figure 1: Debris flow wave in some characteristic sections of the experimental channel. Comparison between mathematical model and experimental results. Water-gravel, abs 200, conc. 40%, slope 15°, smooth bottom.

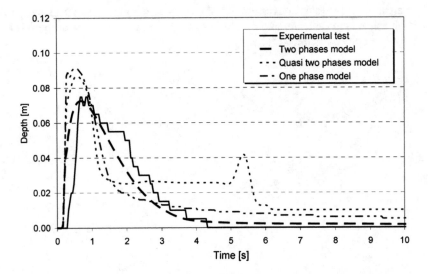

Figure 2:   Debris flow wave in some characteristic sections of the experimental channel. Comparison between mathematical model and experimental results. Water-gravel, abs 140, conc. 40%, slope 20°, smooth bottom.

4   Further development of the model

One of the main features of this paper is to present a two-phase mathematical model, based on the SV equations, suitable to describe the propagation and the profile of debris flow resulting from flash floods such as a sudden collapse of a dam (dam-break). Such an approach has been validated on the ground of laboratory tests, for mature (non-stratified) debris flow. This evidently puts the bases for future research activity and the challenge is to make the tool able to reach, with regard to stratified (immature) flows, the same reliability up to now achieved for the mature ones.

4.1   Stratified (immature) flows

Debris flows are categorized as stratified or immature whenever the solid/liquid mixture is present in the lower layer, while only the water is present in the upper one (figure 3).

Assuming h_{mx} and h_{cw} as the depths of the mixture and of the clear water respectively, the total depth of the debris flow h_{df} is equal to:

$$h_{df} = h_{mx} + h_{cw} \qquad (21)$$

while the maturity degree is assessed as the ratio:

$$d_m = \frac{h_{mx}}{h_{df}} \qquad (22)$$

Larcan et al [15] has suggested – on the basis of laboratory experiments – to distinguish mature and immature debris flow by means of a criterion based on mixture velocity and concentration (figure 4).

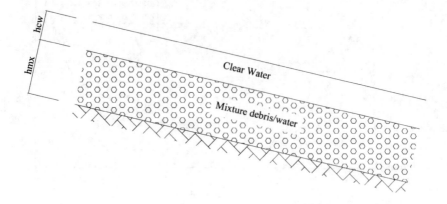

Figure 3: Scheme of the immature (stratified) debris flow.

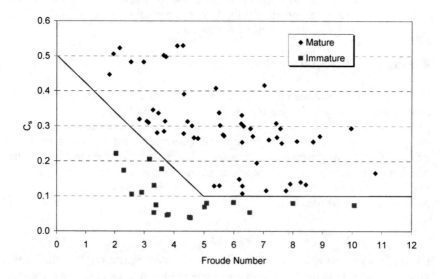

Figure 4: Characteristics of mature and immature debris flows.

The figure underlines the effectiveness of the above mentioned criterion and depicts a boundary between mature and immature debris flow. The boundary can be expressed by:

$$C_{s\,boundary} = \begin{cases} 0.5 - 0.08 \cdot Fr & when \quad Fr < 5 \\ 0.1 & when \quad Fr \geq 5 \end{cases} \tag{23}$$

with Fr: Froude number, while the maturity degree can be assessed as:

$$d_m = \frac{C_{s\,effective}}{C_{s\,boundary}} \qquad (24)$$

The experimental tests showed that in the first phase the flow is stratified; then, usually, it becomes mature, because the velocities and the concentrations are quite high. Finally, the tail of the wave is characterised by low velocities, due to the fact that the solid phase tends to deposit, and thus the flow becomes again stratified.

4.2 Mass and momentum equations for the liquid phase-higher layer (cw)

Mass and momentum equations for clear water can be expressed in conservative form as:

$$\frac{\partial Q_{cw}(s,t)}{\partial s} + \frac{\partial A_{cw}(s,t)}{\partial t} = 0 \qquad (25)$$

$$\frac{\partial Q_{cw}}{\partial t} + \frac{\partial}{\partial s}\left(\beta \cdot \frac{Q_{cw}^2}{A_{cw}}\right) = g \cdot A_{cw} \cdot \left(i - J_{cw} - \frac{\partial H_{cw}}{\partial s} - J_{two\,layers}\right) \qquad (26)$$

The resistance term J_{cw} can be assessed on the basis of bank shear stress, while the slope of the energy line, $J_{two\,layers}$, due to the lower layer, according to Chézy's formula, is expressed as:

$$J_{two\,layers} = \frac{n^2 \cdot (V_{cw} - V_{mx})^2}{R^{4/3}} \qquad (27)$$

being n the Manning's number and V_{mx} the velocity of the lower layer. The drag force $T_{two\,layers}$ between the higher layer and the lower one, can be expressed as:

$$T_{two\,layers} = g \cdot A_{cw} \cdot J_{two\,layers} \qquad (28)$$

4.3 Mass and momentum equations for the liquid phase-lower layer (mx)

In the same ways as (6) and (7), these equations can be expressed as:

$$\frac{\partial Q_{l,mx}(s,t)}{\partial s} + \frac{\partial(c_{l,mx} \cdot A_{mx}(s,t))}{\partial t} = 0 \qquad (29)$$

$$\frac{\partial Q_{l,mx}}{\partial t} + \frac{\partial}{\partial s}\left(\beta \cdot \frac{Q_{l,mx}^2}{c_{l,mx} \cdot A_{mx}}\right) = g \cdot c_{l,mx} \cdot A_{mx} \cdot \left(i - J_{mx} - \frac{\partial H_{mx}}{\partial s}\right) + $$
$$- F + c_{l,mx} \cdot T_{two\,layers} \qquad (30)$$

$T_{two\,layers}$ is opposite in sign with respect to (28) due to the fact that the higher layer, with greater velocities, exerts a drag force to the mixture.

4.4 Mass and momentum equations for the solid phase-lower layer

Likewise (11) and (12), mass and momentum equations can be expressed as:

$$\frac{\partial(c_{s,mx} \cdot A_{mx})}{\partial t} + \frac{\partial Q_{s,mx}}{\partial s} = E \cdot c_* \cdot B \qquad (31)$$

$$\frac{\partial Q_{s,mx}}{\partial t} + \frac{\partial}{\partial s}\left(\beta \cdot \frac{Q_{s,mx}^2}{c_{s,mx} \cdot A_{mx}}\right) = -g \cdot \frac{\rho_s - \rho_l}{\rho_s} \cdot c_{s,mx} \cdot \left(1 + i^2\right) \cdot$$

$$\cdot \frac{\partial H_{mx}}{\partial s} \cdot A_{mx} + F + g \cdot \frac{\rho_s - \rho_l}{\rho_s} \cdot c_{s,mx} \cdot \left(i^2 - 1\right) \cdot tg\delta \cdot A_{mx} + \tag{32}$$

$$+ g \cdot \frac{\rho_s - \rho_l}{\rho_s} \cdot c_{s,mx} \cdot A_{mx} \cdot i + c_{s,mx} \cdot T_{two\ layers}$$

4.5 Numerical model

The SV equations for 1D two-phase unsteady debris flow can be expressed in compact vector form as follows:

$$\frac{\partial \mathbf{V}}{\partial t} + \frac{\partial \mathbf{F'}}{\partial s} + \mathbf{C} \cdot \frac{\partial \mathbf{F''}}{\partial s} = \mathbf{S} \tag{33}$$

where, for a rectangular section channel and for a completely mixed fluid:

$$\mathbf{V} = \begin{pmatrix} c_l \cdot A \\ c_s \cdot A \\ Q_l \\ Q_s \end{pmatrix} \quad \mathbf{F'} = \begin{pmatrix} Q_l \\ Q_s \\ \dfrac{Q_l^2}{c_l \cdot A} \\ \dfrac{Q_s^2}{c_s \cdot A} \end{pmatrix} \quad \mathbf{F''} = \begin{pmatrix} 0 \\ 0 \\ \dfrac{1}{2} \cdot g \cdot \dfrac{A^2}{B} \\ \dfrac{1}{2} \cdot g \cdot \dfrac{\rho_s - \rho_l}{\rho_s} \cdot \left(1 + i^2\right) \cdot \dfrac{A^2}{B} \end{pmatrix}$$

$$\mathbf{S} = \begin{pmatrix} 0 \\ E \cdot c_* \cdot B \\ g \cdot c_l \cdot A \cdot (i - J) - \dfrac{3}{4} \cdot c_D \cdot \left(v_l - v_s\right)^2 \cdot \dfrac{c_s \cdot A}{d_{50}} \\ g \cdot c_s \cdot A \cdot \dfrac{\rho_s - \rho_l}{\rho_s} \cdot \left[\left(i^2 - 1\right) \cdot tg\delta + i\right] + \\ + \dfrac{3}{4} \cdot c_D \cdot \dfrac{\rho_l}{\rho_s} \cdot \left(v_l - v_s\right)^2 \cdot \dfrac{c_s \cdot A}{d_{50}} \end{pmatrix}$$

$$\mathbf{C} = \begin{pmatrix} 0 & 0 & c_l & c_s \end{pmatrix}$$

and for a stratified (immature) flow:

$$\mathbf{V} = \begin{pmatrix} A_{cw} \\ c_{l,mx} \cdot A_{mx} \\ c_{s,mx} \cdot A_{mx} \\ Q_{cw} \\ Q_{l,mx} \\ Q_{s,mx} \end{pmatrix} \quad \mathbf{F'} = \begin{pmatrix} Q_{cw} \\ Q_{l,mx} \\ Q_{s,mx} \\ \dfrac{Q_{cw}^2}{A_{cw}} \\ \dfrac{Q_{l,mx}^2}{c_{l,mx} \cdot A_{mx}} \\ \dfrac{Q_{s,mx}^2}{c_{s,mx} \cdot A_{mx}} \end{pmatrix}$$

$$\mathbf{F''} = \begin{pmatrix} 0 \\ 0 \\ 0 \\ \dfrac{1}{2} \cdot g \cdot \dfrac{A_{cw}^2}{B} \\ \dfrac{1}{2} \cdot g \cdot \dfrac{A_{mx}^2}{B} \\ \dfrac{1}{2} \cdot g \cdot \dfrac{\rho_s - \rho_l}{\rho_s} \cdot \left(1 + i^2\right) \cdot \dfrac{A_{mx}^2}{B} \end{pmatrix}$$

$$\mathbf{S} = \begin{pmatrix} 0 \\ 0 \\ E \cdot c_* \cdot B \\ g \cdot A_{cw} \cdot (i - J_{cw}) - \dfrac{n^2 \cdot \left(V_{cw} - V_{mx}\right)^2}{R_{cw}^{4/3}} \\ g \cdot c_{l,mx} \cdot A_{mx} \cdot (i - J_{mx}) - \dfrac{3}{4} \cdot c_D \cdot \left(v_{l,mx} - v_{s,mx}\right)^2 \cdot \dfrac{c_{s,mx} \cdot A_{mx}}{d_{50}} + \\ c_{l,mx} \cdot g \cdot A_{mx} \cdot \dfrac{n^2 \cdot \left(V_{cw} - V_{mx}\right)^2}{R_{cw}^{4/3}} \\ g \cdot c_{s,mx} \cdot A_{mx} \cdot \dfrac{\rho_s - \rho_l}{\rho_s} \cdot \left[\left(i^2 - 1\right) \cdot tg\delta + i\right] + \dfrac{3}{4} \cdot c_D \cdot \dfrac{\rho_l}{\rho_s} \cdot \left(v_{l,mx} - v_{s,mx}\right)^2 \cdot \\ \dfrac{c_{s,mx} \cdot A_{mx}}{d_{50}} + c_{s,mx} \cdot g \cdot A_{mx} \cdot \dfrac{n^2 \cdot \left(V_{cw} - V_{mx}\right)^2}{R_{cw}^{4/3}} \end{pmatrix}$$

$$\mathbf{C} = \begin{pmatrix} 0 & 0 & 0 & 1 & c_l & c_s \end{pmatrix}$$

Numerical treatments of such equations, generally, require schemes capable of preserving discontinuities, possibly without any special shift (shock-capturing schemes). Most numerical approaches have been developed in the last two or three decades, that include the use of finite differences, finite elements or discrete/distinct element methods [1, 19].

The McCormack predictor-corrector explicit scheme is widely used for solving dam-break problems, due to the fact that it is a shock-capturing technique, with second order accuracy both in time and in space, and that the artificial dissipation terms, the so-called Total Variation Diminishing (TVD) Lax–Wendroff correction, can be introduced, in order to avoid non-physical shocks and oscillations around discontinuities [8, 9].

The main disadvantage of this solver regards the restriction to the time step size in order to satisfy Courant–Friedrichs–Lewy (CFL) stability condition. However, this is not a real problem for dam-break debris flow phenomena that require short time step to describe the evolution of the discharge.

Whatsoever the solver adopted, at each timestep the degree of maturity has to be assessed, in order to choose the appropriate terms to incorporate in the SV equations.

5   Conclusions

Achieving a set of debris flow constitutive equations is a task which has been given particular attention by the scientific community during the second half of the last century.

In this context, the present paper describes the main features and characteristics of a numerical model suitable to solve the SV equations, modified for including two-phase debris flow phenomena, and able to assess the depth of the wave and the velocities of both the liquid and solid phases of non-stratified (mature) flow, following dam-break events.

The model is based on mass and momentum conservation equations for both liquid and solid phases. The McCormack–Jameson two-step explicit scheme with second order accuracy was employed for the solution of the equations, written in a conservative-law form. The technique was applied for determining both the propagation and the profile of a debris flow wave resulting from the instantaneous and complete collapse of a storage dam. Different experimental cases of dam-break situations in a square section channel were considered for the purpose of comparing results.

Agreements between computational and experimental results regarding both wave front-advance and stage hydrographs are considered very satisfactory.

To widen the reach of the proposed model an essential improvement has been outlined in the paper. This improvement will render the model suitable to predict stratified (immature) flow by taking into account mass and momentum conservation equations for each phase and layer. Momentum conservation equations describe energy exchanges between the two phases in the same layer and between layers, while mass conservation equations describe mass exchanges between layers.

Within this ground, in order to analyse reverse grading (sorting) it is necessary to analyse the wave propagation process, when the solid phase is composed of non-homogeneous material. In this case the model should be further improved in order to feature the distribution of the material of different size of the solid phase: larger size material positioned in the front and in the top of the wave, and finer one in the bottom and in the tail.

References

[1]   Asmar B.N., Lanston P.A., Ergenzinger Z., "The potential of the discrete method to simulate debris flow" in Proceeding of the *First International Conference on Debris Flow Hazard Mitigation: Mechanics, Prediction and Assessment*, Eds. Chen, New York, 1997

[2]   Aureli F., Mignosa P., Tomirotti M., "Numerical simulation and experimental verification of dam-break flow with shocks" *Journal of Hydraulic Research*, 2000, 38, pp. 197–216

[3]   Bagnold R.A., "Experiments on a gravity-free dispersion of large solid spheres in a Newtonian fluid under shear" in *Proceedings of the Royal Society of London*, Series A, 225, 1954, pp. 49–63

[4]   Bechteler W., Kulisch H., Nujic M., "2D dam-break flooding wave: comparison between experimental and calculated results" *Floods and Flood Management*, Ed. Saul, Dodrecht, 1992

[5]   Bellos V., Sakkas J.G., "1D dam-break flood propagation on dry bed" *Journal of Hydraulic Engineering*, 1987, ASCE 113(12), pp. 1510 – 1524

[6]   Brufau P., Garcia-Navarro P., Ghilardi P., Natale L., Savi F., "1D Mathematical modelling of debris flow" *Journal of Hydraulic Research*, 38, 2001, pp. 435 – 446

[7]   Egashira S., Ashida K., "Sediment transport in steep slope flumes", Proc. of RoC *Japan Joint Seminar on Water Resources*,1987

[8]   Garcia R., Kahawita R.A., "Numerical solution of the De Saint Venant equations with the McCormack finite-difference scheme" *International Journal of Numerical Methods in Fluids*, 1986, 6, pp. 259–274

[9]   Garcia Navarro P., Saviròn J.M., "McCormack methods for numerical simulation of 1D discontinuous unsteady open channel flow" *Journal of Hydraulic Research*, 1992, 30(1), pp. 313–327

[10] Ghilardi P., Natale L., Savi F., "Two mathematical models simulating a real-world debris-flow", Proc. IAHR Symposium on *River, Coastal and Estuarine Morphodynamics*, Genova, 1999

[11] Gregoretti C., "Fronte di debris-flow. Composizione e celerità", *L'acqua* n. 6, pp. 29–39, 1998 (in Italian)

[12] Gregoretti C., "Stima della velocità massima del fronte di una colata detritica che si propaga in un alveo torrentizio", *Idra 2000* (in Italian)

[13] Jameson A., "Transonic airfoil calculation using the Euler equations" *Numerical Models in Aeronautical Fluid Dynamics*, Ed. P.L. Roe, 1982, Academic Press, New York

[14] Larcan E., Mambretti S., Orsi E., "Leggi di resistenza al moto nelle colate di detriti conseguenti al crollo di dighe. 1. Apparato sperimentale e primi risultati." Proceedings on *28° Convegno di Idraulica e Costruzioni Idrauliche*, Potenza, 16–19 settembre 2002 (in Italian)

[15] Larcan E., Mambretti S., Pulecchi M., "A procedure for the evaluation of debris flow stratification." Proceedings of the 1st International Conference on *Monitoring, Simulation, Prevention and Remediation of Dense and Debris flow* Eds. Lorenzini, Brebbia and Emmauouloudis, 7–9 giugno 2006, Rhodes, Greece

[16] Mambretti S., Larcan E., De Wrachien D., "Debris flow and dam-break surges: Experimental analysis and two-phase modelling" *Quaderni di Idronomia Montana*, 27, pp. 447–462, 2007

[17] Mambretti S., Larcan E., De Wrachien D., "Theoretical and experimental analysis of debris flow: Rehology and two-phase modelling" (in press) *Irrigation and Drainage*, 2008

[18] McCormack R.W., "The effect of viscosity in hypervelocity impact cratering" *AIAA Paper*, 1969, 75–1

[19] Rodriguez C., Blanco A., Garcia R., "Comparison of 1D debris flow modelling approaches using a high resolution and non-oscillatory numerical scheme on the finite volume methods", Proceeding of the *1st International Conference on Monitoring, Simulation, Prevention and Remediation of Dense and Debris Flow*, Eds. Lorenzini and Brebbia, Rhodes, 2006

[20] Takahashi T. *Debris flow* International Association for Hydraulic Research, Balkema, Rotterdam, 1991

[21] Wan Z., Wang Y., *Hyper-concentrated flow* International Association for Hydraulic Research monograph, The Netherlands, 1984

Comparison between FLO-2D and RAMMS in debris-flow modelling: a case study in the Dolomites

M. Cesca & V. D'Agostino
Department of Land and Agro-Forest Environments,
Padova University, Italy

Abstract

This paper presents a comparison of the results obtained through the use of two numerical models for debris flow simulation. FLO-2D and RAMMS were used to carry out a back analysis of a well-documented debris-flow event, which occurred on 5th July 2006 in the Dolomites (Fiames locality, Belluno, Italy). The performances of FLO-2D and RAMMS are tested in terms of adaptation degree to the observed field data.

Keywords: debris flow, numerical modelling, FLO-2D, RAMMS, Dolomites.

1 Introduction

Debris flows are common in mountainous areas and present a severe hazard due to their high mobility and impact energy. In addition to causing significant morphological changes along rivers and mountain slopes, these flows are frequently reported to have brought about extensive property damage and loss of life. Therefore, accurate prediction of runout distances and velocities can reduce these losses by providing a means to delineate hazard areas, to estimate hazard intensity for input into risk studies and to provide parameters for the design of protective measures.

Application of computational debris-flow models to real case studies necessitates many assumptions about the details of the event and the pre-event topography. Debris flow routing models are necessary for engineering practice and some models have been in regular use for a number of years, e.g., for producing hazard maps or for evaluating the effectiveness of mitigation

WIT Transactions on Engineering Sciences, Vol 60, © 2008 WIT Press
www.witpress.com, ISSN 1743-3533 (on-line)
doi:10.2495/DEB080201

structures. Numerical modelling is useful to understand the rheological behaviour of a debris flow event. The comparison of different debris flow models with well-documented case studies is of value. The objective of this paper is to evaluate the suitability of 2D numerical models to replicate a well-documented event that occurred in the Dolomites, Italy. The Fiames debris-flow event of 5th July 2006 was simulated using FLO-2D and RAMMS. The FLO-2D model, a commercial code in widespread practical use, is a finite difference debris and mud flow simulation program based on a quadratic rheologic law (O'Brien et al [1]). RAMMS was developed in 2005 by the Swiss Federal Institute for Forest, Snow and Landscape Research (WSL, Birmensdorf) and the Swiss Federal Institute for Snow and Avalanche Research (SLF, Davos). RAMMS uses a one-phase approach based on Voellmy rheology (Voellmy [2], Salm et al [3]). After calibration, the performances of FLO-2D and RAMMS are tested in terms of simulations adaptation to the observed field data using two different datasets of input parameters.

2   Numerical simulation models

We carried out numerical simulations using two different models, FLO-2D and RAMMS. The tested models have different approaches: the first describes the routing behaviour of a bulked inflow hydrograph as a homogeneous, one-phase material over a rigid bed; the second has an input file that combines the total volume of the debris flow located in a release area.

2.1 The FLO-2D model

FLO-2D is a flood-routing model, which uses a dynamic-wave momentum equation and a finite-difference routing scheme. Its formulation is based on the depth-averaged open channel flow equations of continuity and momentum for unsteady conditions developed on a Eulerian framework. The adopted numerical analysis technique is a non-linear explicit difference method. FLO-2D assumes the following constitutive equation (quadratic model):

$$\tau = \tau_c + \mu_N (du/dy) + C(du/dy)^2 \qquad (1)$$

where τ is the total shear stress (Pa), τ_c the yield stress (Pa), μ_N the dynamic viscosity (Pa s), du/dy the shear rate (s[-1]) and C the inertial stress coefficient. Rewriting eqn. (1) in terms of depth-integrated dissipative friction slope (S_f) it follows (O'Brien et al [1]):

$$S_f = \frac{\tau_c}{\gamma_m \, h} + \frac{K \, \mu_N \, u}{8 \, \gamma_m \, h^2} + \frac{n_d^2 \, u^2}{h^{4/3}} \qquad (2)$$

with γ_m being the specific debris flow weight; h the flow depth, u the mean flow velocity, K the resistance parameter for laminar flow, n_d the turbulent dispersive n of Manning. Viscosity and critical shear stress of eqn. (2) are supported by laboratory measurements (O'Brien and Julien [4]), correlating these variables with the sediment concentration by volume of the flow. The main rheological input parameters of FLO-2D are τ_c and μ_N. An additional variable called 'surface detention' allows to assess a minimum depth of the flow for flood routing. When setting its value, each square cell of the computational domain works as a reservoir for h less or equal than the surface detention depth.

2.2 The software package RAMMS

RAMMS (Rapid Mass Movements) is an unified software package that combines three-dimensional process modules for snow avalanches, debris flows and rockfalls, together with a protect module (forest, dams, barriers) and a visualization module in one tool. For debris-flow simulation, RAMMS actually uses a one-phase approach (similar to avalanches, Voellmy-Fluid). The Voellmy-Fluid model assumes no shear deformation. The flow body moves as a plug with everywhere the same mean velocity (u) over the height of the flow (h); the friction slope S_f is given by:

$$S_f = \mu \ \cos\varphi + \frac{u^2}{\xi \, h} \qquad (3)$$

where φ is the downslope angle (positive) of the terrain. The flow law is a well calibrated, hydraulics-based, depth-averaged continuum model and divides the debris flow resistance into a dry Coulomb-type friction (μ) and a viscous resistance (ξ), which varies with the square of the flow velocity. A finite volume scheme is used to solve the shallow water equations in general three-dimensional terrain. The input parameters of RAMMS are the total volume of the debris flow (located in one or more release areas with an assigned mean depth of the sediments) and the resistance parameters μ and ξ.

3   Study area and event reconstruction

The study area is located on the left side of the Boite River Valley just upstream of the town of Cortina d'Ampezzo (Fiames locality, Belluno, Italy). An intense rainstorm triggered six debris flows during the afternoon of 5th July 2006. Three main morphological units can be identified in the study area (fig. 1). Rock basins, composed by dolomite and limestone rocks, are present in the upper part. A thick talus, consisting of particles from silt to boulders (with size up to 1–2 m), is located below the rock cliffs. The lower part of the slope is formed by coalescing fans built by debris flows, whose initiation points are placed at the contact between the rock cliffs and the scree slope. The flow originated from six rock basins (fig. 1). The area of the rock basins range from 0.024 km² to 0.182 km² (table 1). The maximum elevation is between 1984 m and 2400 m a.s.l., and the minimum elevation, which corresponds to the initiation area of debris flows, is from 1521 m to 1624 m a.s.l. The channel length varies between 110 m and 540 m and the mean channel slope from 22° to 28°.

The climatic conditions are typical of an alpine environment: the annual precipitation at Cortina ranges between 900 mm and 1500 mm, with an average of 1100 mm; snowfalls occurs normally from October to May; intense summer thunderstorms are common and provide a maximum to the seasonal precipitation regime.

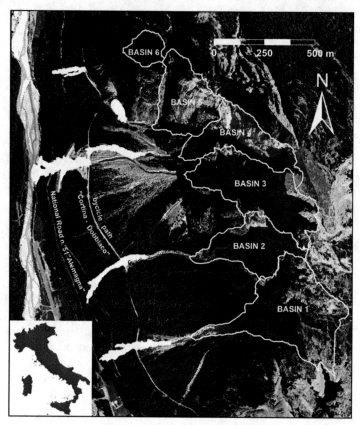

Figure 1:   Location of the study area with rock basins and debris-flow deposits outlined.

Table 1:   Values of basin area A_C, deposited volume V, flooded area A_d, mean sediment thickness h_d, maximum debris-flow sediment concentration at equilibrium condition $c_{e\ max}$ and estimated debris-flow peak discharge $Q_{d\ max}$ for each basin.

Catchment	A_C (km^2)	V (m^3)	A_d (m^2)	h_d (m)	$c_{e\ max}$ (-)	$Q_{d\ max}$ (m^3 s^{-1})
1	0.182	15000	10116	1.39	0.665	32
2	0.087	10600	8543	1.19	0.700	21
3	0.147	46800	16934	2.57	0.710	100
4	0.092	11000	6785	1.50	0.700	22
5	0.091	5200	4609	1.00	0.630	12
6	0.024	2100	3751	0.50	0.725	16

Immediately after the 2006 event, field surveys were carried out in the study area. These surveys made it possible to measure several features of debris-flow deposits: mean and maximum depth, depth and slope of the deposition lobes and cross sections on the deposits. Moreover, cross-sections were measured along the main channel and a detailed description of debris-flow initiation areas were carried out. The boundaries of the debris-flow deposits were mapped using a handy GPS. The other geometric characteristics were measured using a laser distance meter and a tape.

The LiDAR and photographic data was acquired from a helicopter using an ALTM 3100 OPTECH and Rollei H20 digital camera flying at an average altitude of 1000 m above ground level during snow free conditions in October 2006. The flying speed was 80 knots, the scan angle 20 degrees and the scan rate 71 KHz. The survey design point density was specified to be greater than 5 points per m^2. LiDAR point measurements were filtered into returns from vegetation and bare ground using the Terrascan^{TM} software classification routines and algorithms.

The debris flows of July 5th, 2006 were triggered by an intense thunderstorm and hailstorm lasting from 6 p.m. to 7 p.m. The highest values of rainfall intensity during the event were 12.5 mm/5' and 64 mm/h. These values were measured at a meteorological station located approximately 1 km from the study area.

The debris flows initiated at the outlet of the rock basins, through the mobilization of loose debris into the flow with progressive entraining of debris from channel bank erosion and bed scour. The main channel stopped (at an altitude between 1441 m and 1553 m a.s.l.) where the slope angle decreases and consequently the depositional zone begins.

The deposited volume was assessed by subtracting the 5 meter grid DEM of the post-event ground surface elevation (LiDAR data) with the pre-event DEM, derived from a topographic map on the scale of 1:5000.

Water runoff from the rock basin was simulated by means of a hydrological model, which uses the CN method of the Soil Conservation Service (Chow et al [5]) to estimate the rainfall excess and a unit hydrograph to compute the flood hydrograph. On the basis of geological setting and land use of the basin upstream of the triggering point, we obtained an average value of CN = 84. The amount of the initial abstraction was set to the 10% of potential maximum retention to assess the excess rainfall. The concentration time was evaluated as the ratio between the main channel length and the flow velocity along the slopes (assumed to be equal to 2 m/s). The flood hydrograph was computed with a unit hydrograph (Chow et al [5]) extracted from a hypsographic curve by assuming the equivalence between the contour lines and the lines with the same concentration time. After the computation of six flood hydrographs, the following relation was adopted to infer debris-flow discharge from the water flood discharge (Takahashi [6]):

$$Q_d = \frac{Q_w}{1 - \dfrac{c_e}{c_*}} \tag{4}$$

where Q_d is the debris flow discharge associated to the liquid discharge Q_w; c_* and c_e are the "in situ" volumetric concentration of bed sediments before the flood and the debris-flow sediment concentration at equilibrium conditions respectively. Eqn. (4) refers to steady uniform conditions of a debris flow generated by a sudden release of Q_w from the upstream end of an erodible and saturated grain bed. The assumption in eqn. (4) of a constant ratio c_e/c_* for the entire duration of the flood would be too severe a hypothesis in relation to the type of debris flow surges observed in the streams of the Dolomites (D'Agostino and Marchi [7]). Therefore the debris flow graph was plotted assuming a linear variation of c_e/c_* from a minimum value ($c_{e\ min} = 0.2$) to a maximum ($c_{e\ max}$) for each basin according to eqn. (4). The concentration $c_{e\ max}$ was calibrated to match the deposited debris-flow volumes with the reconstructed ones.

Table 1 reports, for each catchment, the basin area A_C, the deposited volume V, the flooded area A_d, the mean thickness h_d of the debris-flow deposits ($h_d = V/A_d$), the maximum debris-flow sediment concentration at equilibrium conditions $c_{e\ max}$ and the estimated debris-flow peak discharge $Q_{d\ max}$.

4 Models application

Model calibration was carried out by comparing observed and computed characteristics of the deposits in terms of mean depth, flooded area, overall volume and shape of their boundaries. The calibration involved different input parameters for FLO-2D and RAMMS, because they follow different approaches and rheological laws. The computational domain in FLO-2D was assumed wholly as floodplain in order to achieve an unbiased comparison with RAMMS.

4.1 Input parameters

The adopted cell size was always 5 m in FLO-2D (vers.2006). To reproduce the terrain roughness, the following n values were assigned on the basis of land use (fig.1) in the depositional zone: $n = 0.08$ m$^{-1/3}$s for debris areas, $n = 0.14$ m$^{-1/3}$s for shrubs and $n = 0.33$ m$^{-1/3}$s for forest. FLO-2D calibration was focused on the rheological parameters of viscosity and critical shear stress proposed by O'Brien [8]. Since the Fiames debris flows stopped at high slopes, always greater than $16°$, the preliminary best simulations were carried out using the rheological scheme named "Aspen Pit 1" (O'Brien and Julien [4]) and setting K=24 in eqn. (2) (larger K values do not improve the quality of the results). In all cases this rheology reproduced deposits with an elongated shape and consequently overestimated runout distances. During the back analysis it has been noted that surface detention has a strong influence on the results and it can be used as a surrogate of the rheology. When the surface detention value increases the computed deposits assume a lower extent very quickly. As reported in table 2, the calibrated values of surface detention ranges between 0.10 m and 0.50 m.

RAMMS model (beta vers.2007) calibration was related to the parameters which describe the debris-flow resistance. The dry friction factor (μ) was calculated as the surface slope of each debris-flow deposits along the terminal

Table 2:   Calibrated surface detention values using the FLO-2D model for the Fiames debris-flow event (5th July 2006).

Input parameter	Catchment					
	1	2	3	4	5	6
Surface detention (m)	0.15	0.10	0.50	0.15	0.40	0.35

path (30–40 m). The turbulent friction factor (ξ) was chosen and assessed in a range between 15 and 1000 m/s^2 according to typical values quoted in literature (Ayotte and Hungr [9]). Table 3 summarised the calibrated input parameters for RAMMS. The adopted cell size ranges from 5 m to 20 m and it affects the shape of flooded areas markedly.

Table 3:   Calibrated input parameters using the RAMMS model for the Fiames debris-flow event (5th July 2006).

Input parameters	Catchment					
	1	2	3	4	5	6
μ (= tan θ_{df})	0.18	0.20	0.19	0.37	0.39	0.45
ξ (m/s^2)	500	40	15	40	100	1000
Cell size (m)	20	10	10	10	5	5

4.2 Comparison between FLO-2D and RAMMS simulations

In spite of repeated attempts of calibrations the computed flooded area has been overestimated: between 27% and 376% for FLO-2D and from 254% to 1552% for RAMMS (table 4). This behaviour is partially due to the cell size. In fact the maximum overestimation with RAMMS occurred for the basin 1 (fig.1 and

Table 4:   Comparison between h and A value with h_d and A_d of table 1; h is the simulated mean thickness and A is the simulated flooded area.

Catchment	Variable	FLO-2D		RAMMS	
		Value	%	Value	%
1	h (m)	0.430	-69%	0.073	-95%
	A (m^2)	48150	+376%	167142	+ 1552%
2	h (m)	0.444	-63%	0.112	-91%
	A (m^2)	30225	+254%	92968	+988%
3	h (m)	3.518	+37%	0.140	-95%
	A (m^2)	21425	+27%	59930	+254%
4	h (m)	0.377	-75%	0.118	-92%
	A (m^2)	19000	+180%	76946	+1034%
5	h (m)	0.434	-57%	0.218	-78%
	A (m^2)	10955	+138%	21986	+377%
6	h (m)	0.548	+10%	0.111	-77%
	A (m^2)	8475	+126%	17223	+359%

WIT Transactions on Engineering Sciences, Vol 60, © 2008 WIT Press
www.witpress.com, ISSN 1743-3533 (on-line)

table 1) where the topographic detail was low (cell size = 20 m). A 5 m cell size causes avulsion phenomena along the main channel also in FLO-2D (fig. 2). The mean thickness of the deposits was generally underestimated with the exception of two cases simulated with FLO-2D (catchments 3 and 6; table 4). This underestimation is a consequence of the overabundant extent of the simulated flooded area since the debris-flow volume is the main input parameter in both models. In FLO-2D simulations the underestimation of mean thickness varied between 57% and 75% (mean value 66%), while for RAMMS the percentage was higher (between 78% and 95%, mean value 88%). This analysis corroborates that RAMMS simulates wide and fan-shaped deposits similar to those produced by avalanches. It is also interesting to note that exclusively in the RAMMS simulations a portion of the total debris-flow volume stops is in the propagation channel.

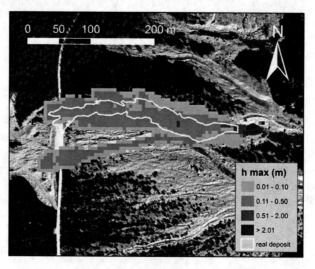

Figure 2: Simulated deposit using FLO-2D: catchment 4.

The following images (fig. 3) show the more satisfactorily simulation with FLO-2D (fig.3a) and a comparison with the RAMMS simulation (fig.3b). The flooded area is always overestimated: FLO-2D produces deposits that are similar to the real ones, whilst simulated deposits using RAMMS have constantly excessive lateral dispersions.

5 Discussion and conclusion

Numerical models benefit from the application to real cases to assist in understanding their potentials and limitations. A back analysis was carried out on six well documented debris flows in the Dolomites using FLO-2D and RAMMS models. To being with, an accurate representation of the topography is vital to obtain a reasonable representation of the observed deposition patterns. In fact, a

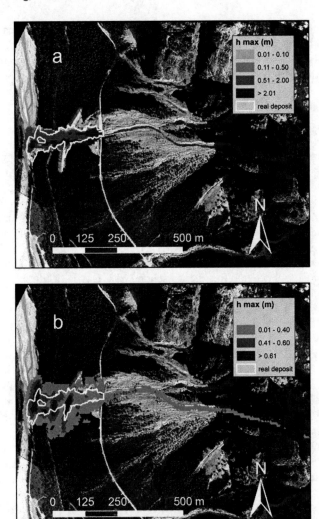

Figure 3:   Comparison between FLO-2D (a) and RAMMS (b); catchment 3.

detailed description of the propagation areas improves the results of both numerical models. FLO-2D gives the best results even if the rheological variables – viscosity and yield stress coupled with the surface detention depth – need further investigations on their physical significance. The six debris flows halt on steep slopes (> 16°) and their depositional process is conditioned and encouraged by the forest in the depositional area, the water draining from the mixture during the movement and the topographic irregularity (roads, fan morphology, stream cross section). The surface detention has a large influence on runout distances and maximum lateral dispersions. In RAMMS simulations the entire input solid volume is located in a restricted area and not timed as in a

FLO-2D input hydrograph. Therefore the released debris flow suddenly reaches a channel that is insufficient to contain the entire discharge. As a consequence avulsion phenomena occur along the channel and they generate a larger lateral spreading than that observed in the field.

References

[1] O'Brien, J.S., Julien, P.Y. & Fullerton, W.T., Two-dimensional water flood and mudflow simulation. *Journal of Hydraulic Engineering*, **119(2)**, pp. 244–261, 1993.

[2] Voellmy, A., Ueber die Zerstoeerunskraft von Lawinen Schweizerische Bauzeitung. English version "On the destructive force of avalanches" translated by Tate R.E. (1964), ed. US Department of Agriculture Forest Service, 1955.

[3] Salm, B., Butkard, A. & Gubler, H., Berechnung von Fliesslawinen, eine Anleitung für Praktiker mit Beispielen. Mitteilung 47, Eigdenossichen Institut für Schnee und Lawinenforschung SLF Davos, 1990.

[4] O'Brien, J.S. & Julien, P.Y., Laboratory analysis of mudflows properties. *Journal of Hydraulic Engineering*, **114(8)**, pp. 877–887, 1988.

[5] Chow, V.T., Maidment, D.R. & Mays, L.W., *Applied hydrology*, McGraw-Hill: New York, pp. 201–236, 1988.

[6] Takahashi, T., Mechanical characteristics of debris flow. *Journal of Hydraulic Division*, **104**, pp. 1153–1169, 1978.

[7] D'Agostino, V. & Marchi, L., Validation of semi-empirical relationships for the definition of debris-flow behaviour in granular materials. *Proc. of the 3rd Int. Conf. on Debris Flows Hazard Mitigation: Mechanics, Prediction and Assessment*, eds. D. Rickenmann & C.L. Chen, Millpress: Rotterdam, pp. 1097–1106, 2003.

[8] O'Brien, J.S., Physical processes, rheology and modelling of mudflows. Doctoral dissertation, Colorado State University, Fort Collins, Colorado, 1986.

[9] Ayotte, D. & Hungr, L., Calibration of a runout prediction model for debris flow and avalanches, *Proc. of the 2nd Int. Conf. on Debris Flows Hazard Mitigation: Mechanics, Prediction and Assessment*, eds. G.F. Wieczorek & N.D. Naeser, Balkema: Rotterdam, pp. 505–514, 2000.

Role and management of in-channel wood in relation to flood events in Southern Andes basins

L. Mao[1], F. Comiti[1], A. Andreoli[2], L. Picco[1], M. A. Lenzi[1],
A.Urciulo[3], R. Iturraspe[3] & A. Iroumè[4]
[1]Department of Land and Agroforest Environment,
University of Padova, Italy
[2]Universidad de Concepcion, Chile
[3]Subsecretaría de Recursos Naturales de Tierra del Fuego,
Ushuaia, Argentina
[4]Instituto de Manejo Forestal, Universidad Austral de Chile, Chile

Abstract

This paper analyses the connection among wood dynamics, channel morphology
and flood risk in mountain basins of the Southern Chilean Andes and of the
Argentinean Tierra del Fuego. Guidelines for the management of in-channel
wood and of the riparian buffer strip are suggested, along with considerations
about possible input from landslides and debris flows. A selection of low-impact
check dams specifically designed for the retention of floating LW elements is
finally provided.
Keywords: woody debris, mountain rivers, flood risk, control works.

1 Introduction

Large wood (LW) in mountain streams plays – especially when organized in
jams – relevant geomorphic and biological roles which enhance the ecological
status of natural channels by increasing morphological diversity and complexity
[6]. LW accumulations strongly affect also flow hydraulics and transport/storage
of sediments within the channel system, thus conditioning channel dimensions
[12] and typology and distribution of bedforms [11]. These beneficial effects
persist from low to high flows, and throughout the entire channel network.

WIT Transactions on Engineering Sciences, Vol 60, © 2008 WIT Press
www.witpress.com, ISSN 1743-3533 (on-line)
doi:10.2495/DEB080211

On the other hand, LW elements may be a source of risk during intense flood periods and in localised areas only. Wood may increase flood risk by a variety of processes, such as flow and sediment surges following collapse of temporary wood dams, inclusion and strengthening of debris flows, clogging on bridge piers and other structures, local bed scour and local bank erosion. Of course, the risks associated to in-channel wood are strongly dependent on the degree of human presence within a catchment (frequency and type of road crossings, proximity and density of humans adjacent to the channels). Therefore, it is evident how a balanced, integrated management of in-channel wood and of the adjacent input areas is absolutely needed. Furthermore, an ecologically-oriented management approach is especially required for mountain basins still presenting a high degree of naturalness such as in the Southern Andes, which represent an ideal location for studying LW in mountain channels draining old-growth forested basins.

2   Wood storage in Southern Andes streams

Recently, field investigations shed light on storage and effects of large wood in mountain streams of Southern Andes [1, 5, 8]. Three study basins were examined (fig. 1), one located in Tierra del Fuego near the city of Ushuaia (Buena Esperanza), and two in the Araucania region of Chile (Tres Arroyos and Rio Toro) that differ with regard to fires disturbance history. Table 1 provides a summary of the main characteristics of the basins.

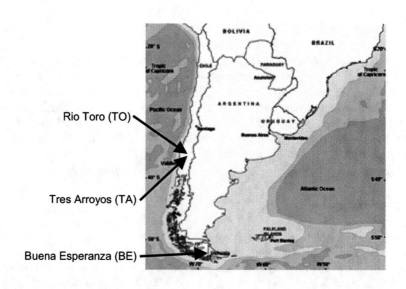

Figure 1:   Location of the investigated basins.

Table 1:   Basins characteristics.

Basin characteristics	Tres Arroyos (TA)	Toro (TO)	Buena Esperanza (BE)
Basin Area (km^2)	9.1	11.1	12.9
Mean basin slope (%)	43	20	23
Climate	Temperate warm humid	Temperate warm humid	Temperate cold humid
Hydrological regime	pluvial/nival	pluvial/nival	glacionival
Annual Precipitation	2217	2480	530/1300
Geology	Volcanic / pyroclastic	Volcanic / pyroclastic	Sedimentary/ Metamorphic
Forest disturbances	Wildfire (1920's)	Wildfire (2002)	Wind blowdowns (?)
Average channel slope (m/m)	0.08	0.05	0.065
Average channel width (m)	7.7	11.9	6.3

In-channel wood quantity in old-growth forested mountain basins of Southern Andes can vary considerably both between and within channels. LW storage in the Tres Arroyos (around 700 m^3 ha^{-1} in the active channel, or 556 m^3 km^{-1} based on channel length) is extremely abundant. Comparably high values have been reported only for old-growth redwood forests in the Pacific Northwest, where average wood storage of up to 1,000 m^3 ha^{-1} were recorded [7]. The relatively low LW volume stored in the Buena Esperanza (120 m^3 ha^{-1}; 76 m^3 km^{-1}) is determined by small log diameters, in turn deriving from the extremely slow growth of nothofagus in the Tierra del Fuego, notwithstanding the extremely high abundance of wood pieces [5, 8]. The Rio Toro is instead characterized by a relatively low supply of large wood that overall makes its LW storage comparable to the Buena Esperanza (117 m^3 ha^{-1}; 144 m^3 km^{-1}).

The high LW storage in the Tres Arroyos can be partly attributed to the small fraction of wood pieces moved by "ordinary" floods. As a term of comparison, in the Mack Creek, a third-order stream that flows through a old-growing coniferous forest, the average wood storage is very high (812 m^3 ha^{-1}; [6]) because of the small fraction of LW elements moved by ordinary events (<1%; [6]. In the Tres Arroyos, similarly low percentage of wood pieces (2.5-4%) is mobilized each year by ordinary floods, while a greater fraction of logs are transported by flow in the Buena Esperanza (10%) probably due, once again, to the smaller dimensions of the logs, so easier to be moved.

The strong longitudinal variation of LW quantity in the Tres Arroyos and in the Buena Esperanza, as well as its link to "external" factors (occasional large trees fallen into the channel, debris flows confluences and landslides) rather than to channel properties [5, 8], reflects what observed in 2nd – 4th order channels of the Italian Dolomites [4].

Interestingly, differences may be substantial even in adjacent basins, and less pronounced between different climates and forest type (i.e. latitudes). Latitude surely acts on tree growth (i.e. wood diameter) and on natural forest disturbance processes (i.e. wildfire vs. windblown moving southward), but notwithstanding different log size and log number the net effect on channel morphology is apparently very similar. In the sub-Antarctic climate of Tierra del Fuego, wood rarely reach large dimensions [5, 8] but its abundant supply by wind-caused mortality [14] make streams prone to be locally grade-controlled by valley jams (Fig. 2(a)) and log steps (Fig. 2(b)) composed of floated debris trapped by occasional fallen trees.

Figure 2:   Valley jam (a) and log step (b) in the Buena Esperanza main channel.

In the warmer climate of the Araucania, fires command forest regeneration and thus probably wood supply to channels. However, in-channel wood loading does not respond immediately to wildfire but a certain lag time of several decades exists [2, 16]. This may explain why wood volumes are so different between the Rio Toro – where almost all the basin forests burned in 2002 – and the Tres Arroyos, which is now heavily dissected as a consequence of fires occurred almost a century ago. Of course, basin geology and topography plays a fundamental role in delivering burned dead wood from the hillslope to the main channel. In the Rio Toro the burned trees are still standing (fig. 3(a)), and no landslides have taken place yet in the basin, possibly as a consequence of the smaller basin slope (fig. 3).

In contrast, in the Tres Arroyos, the destruction of the forest cover caused severe slope instability (fig. 4) that in turn resulted in debris flow phenomena able to transport many huge pieces of wood into the stream, prompting the formation of massive valley jams. An enormous accumulation of LW (gross geometrical volume ~600 m^3), formed by 100–150 wood pieces 0.5 m in diameter and 4–5 m long on average, lies at the confluence of this debris flow channel with the main Tres Arroyos channel. Figure 5 shows two images of the channel depicting the stream upstream of the confluence through the old-growth stands (a), and the stream downstream of the valley jam (b). The location of the valley jams is clearly linked to external forcings such as landslides, actively eroded banks and the confluences with debris flow channels, which provide the

Figure 3:   View of the Rio Toro basin.

Figure 4:   Landslides and minor debris flow on the hillslopes of the Tres Arroyos.

main channel with large, stable wood pieces able to build up a large transversal jam structure by trapping smaller wood pieces [1].

3   Wood management options

The previous section has illustrated how in-channel woody debris represents a fundamental component of the upland channel networks morphology and processes in the Southern Andes. In contrast to European basins, much of the original geomorphological and ecological richness deriving from an abundant presence of wood in the stream network can still be found in many parts of the temperate Andes. At the same time, the human presence is there rapidly encroaching pristine or semi-pristine basins, thus increasing flood risk by building infrastructures and residential structures within fluvial corridors (i.e. active floodplains and channels) and on alluvial fans, parts of the landscape which are naturally subject to potentially dangerous transport of sediment and wood during major flood events (i.e., recurrence interval >20–30 yr).

Figure 5:   Downstream (a) and upstream (b) view of a big valley jam in the Tres Arroyos channel.

Therefore, the first management option against flood risk – not only due to floating wood – is avoid building any valuable structure in flood-prone areas, i.e. the adoption of a careful land use planning. However, if something is already located in the fluvial corridor because of ill-advised decisions of the past, priority should be given to assess whether its removal (i.e. relocation) is feasible, because this option is often the most sustainable in the long run. For minor infrastructure, some solutions as debris sweepers at bridge piers and racks at culverts [3] might be sufficient. A change in building typology could also be a good strategy (e.g., a suspension bridge instead of having piers).

In the case buildings and/or infrastructures of major relevance cannot be relocated and wood is recognized to represent a significant hazard during major floods (20–100 yr return interval), the adoption of structural countermeasures is needed, after an evaluation of where and how much wood will enter the network, as well as where critical cross-sections for obstructions are situated. Because these control works can be expensive, their construction must be justified by a cost-benefit analysis. Next section will provide a brief overview on the principal control works for the wood entrapment and on the parameters to be considered in the choice of the most appropriate type.

Removal of wood and of riparian trees from the channel, typically viewed as "ordinary maintenance" of the entire stream network, should be adopted only locally where it is clear that a dangerous jam is being formed at a critical cross-section. Furthermore, such operation is an expensive, mostly useless activity, with negative effects on stream morphology, stability and ecological status.

These considerations are organised as a flow chart in Figure 6, developed for basins <200–300 km^2.

4   Control works for the retention of driftwood

In those cases where the removal/relocation of vulnerable human elements is not socially or technically feasible, the installation of localized control works is often the most recommendable alternative (Fig. 6). In-channel control works for

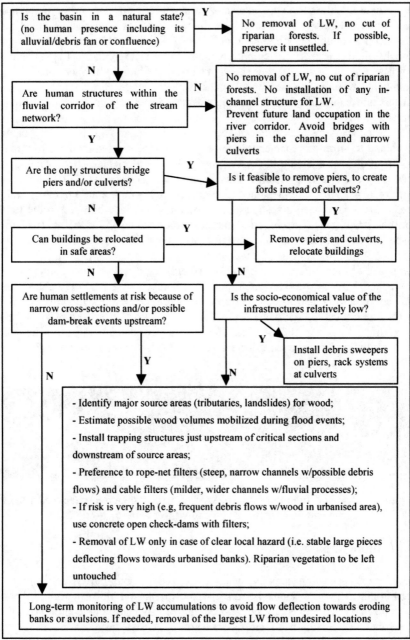

Figure 6:   Large wood management options.

retention of wood transported during major floods have been developed in the densely populated European and Japanese Alps. The choice of the most appropriate retention structure depends on channel width and on the amount of large wood potentially transportable by flood events. As previously pointed out, this second variable is highly variable between basins, but can be evaluated thought field surveys [5] or interpretation of aerial photos [13]. Airborne multispectral imagery [9] has been also tested, but with poor success. In mountain basins of the Southern Andes, filter concrete check dams, rope net barriers and cable filter dams may be selected depending on the basin/channel characteristics.

Filter check dams are commonly built in the European Alps to "break" debris flows and to store the coarser fraction of the transported sediments. From their modification with inclined buttresses and grids, wood-oriented check dams have been developed to trap floating logs in mountain rivers (Fig. 7(a)). Rope net barriers (Fig. 7(b)) are designed for gravel and wood entrapment in small streams, and have been investigated [15] by physical modelling and in the field. For their design, the main required parameters are the height of the net (which is based on the gradient of the torrent), the potential amount of wood to be entrapped, and the design discharge [15]. Cable filter dams (Fig. 7(c)) are composed of harmonic steel cables (Ø ~10 cm) fixed on the river banks by tie-beams and fixed at the river centreline on a buttress to reduce the cables span. This configuration also forces the trapped wood to accumulate towards the river banks where it can be removed. Two of these structures have been recently built along the Sarca River (Italian Alps, Trento) and have demonstrated to efficiently exert a filtering action even during a severe flood with intense wood transport [10].

Figure 7:   Wood retention control works: a filter concrete check dam (a), a rope net barrier (b), and a cable filter dam (c).

5   Conclusions

Dead wood pieces, especially when organized in jams, play an important geomorphic role in streams because of the effects on flow hydraulics, pool formation and sediments storage and ecological diversity and complexity. The three analysed Southern Andes basins show that very large variations in the volume of LW per unit of streambed area occur even within single streams, and that massive inputs may result from slope instabilities adjacent to the channels. Major differences in wood abundance exist due to the basins' disturbance history, and massive wood volumes (i.e., >1000 m^3ha^{-1}) can be reached in basins disturbed by fires followed by mass movements and debris flows. In-channel wood in Andean basins is a precious resource for stream stability and ecological status which should be preserved. However, hazards linked to in-channel wood might likely depend on local, massive inputs of whole portions of forested slopes adjacent to the channels due to mass wasting processes. Prevention and monitoring of hillslope instabilities thus becomes a critical aspect of flood risk mitigation also in relation with wood transport, and is more effective than frequent, anti-ecological cuts of the riparian vegetation. Only in case of high risks for human settlements and infrastructures, wood-trapping structures might be worth to be installed upstream of sensitive locations.

References

[1]   Andreoli A., Comiti F. & Lenzi M.A., Characteristic, distribution and geomorphic role of large woody debris in a mountain stream of the Chilean Andes. *Earth Surface Processes and Landforms*, 33(11), pp. 1675–1692, 2007.

[2]   Benda L., Miller D., Sias J., Martin D., Bilby R., Veldhuisen C., Dunne T., Wood recruitment processes and wood budgeting. In *The Ecology and Management of Wood in World Rivers*, ed. S.V. Gregory, K.L. Boyer, A.M. Gurnell, American Fisheries Society: Bethesda, MD, pp. 49–73, 2003.

[3]   Bradley J.B., Richard D.L., Bahner C.D., Debris control structure, Evaluation and countermeasures. Hydraulic Engineering Circular 9. U.S. D.T., Federal Highway Administration, pp. 179, 2005.

[4]   Comiti F., Andreoli A., Lenzi M.A. & Mao L., Spatial density and characteristics of woody debris in five mountain rivers of the Dolomites (Italian Alps). *Geomorphology*, 78, pp. 44–63, 2006.

[5]   Comiti F., Andreoli A., Mao L. & Lenzi M.A., Wood storage in three mountain streams of the Southern Andes and its hydro-morphological effects. *Earth Surface Processes and Landforms*, 33(2), pp. 244–262, 2008.

[6]   Gurnell, A.M., Piegay, H., Gregory, S.V. & Swanson F.J., Large wood and fluvial processes. *Freshwater Biology*, 47, pp. 601–619, 2002.

[7]   Gurnell A.M., Wood storage and mobility. In *The Ecology and Management of Wood in World Rivers*, ed. S.V. Gregory, K.L. Boyer, A.M. Gurnell, American Fisheries Society: Bethesda, MD, pp. 75–91, 2003.

[8]   Mao L., Andreoli A., Comiti F., Lenzi M.A., Geomorphic effects of large wood jams on a sub-antarctic mountain stream. *River Research and Applications*, in press.

[9]   Marcus, A.W., Marston, R.A., Colvard Jr, C.R. & Gray, R.D., Mapping the spatial and temporal distributions of woody debris in streams of the Greater Yellowstone Ecosystem, USA. *Geomorphology*, 44, pp. 323–335, 2002.

[10] Mazzalai P., Cristofori V., Pecorari E., Lenzi M.A., Briglia a fune sul fiume sarca per la trattenuta di detriti legnosi. *Quaderni di Idronomia Montana*, 26, 425–438, 2006.

[11] Montgomery, D.R., Buffington, J.M., Smith, R.D., Schmidt, K.M. & Pess G., Pool spacing in forest channels. *Water Resources Research*, 31(4), pp. 1097–1105, 1995.

[12] Nakamura, F. & Swanson, F.J., Effects of coarse woody debris on morphology and sediment storage of a mountain stream system in western Oregon. *Earth Surface Processes and Landforms*, 18, pp. 43–61, 1993.

[13] Pecorari E., Comiti F., Rigon E., Picco L. & Lenzi M.A., Caratterizzazione e quantificazione del legname in alveo in corsi d'acqua di grandi dimensioni: risultati preliminari sul fiume Piave, Italia. *Quaderni di Idronomia Montana*, 27/1, 477–488, 2007.

[14] Rebertus, A.J., Kitzberger, T., Veblen, T.T. & Roovers, L.M., Blowdown history and landscape patterns in the Andes of Tierra del Fuego, Argentina. *Ecology*, 78(3), pp. 678–692, 1997.

[15] Rimbock, A., Design of rope net barriers for woody debris entrapment. Introduction of a design concept. *Proc. of the 10th Interpraevent Symposium*, Riva del Garda, Italy, pp. 265–276, 2004.

[16] Zelt, R.B. & Wohl, E.E., Channel and woody debris characteristics in adjacent burned and unburned watersheds a decade after wildfire, Park County, Wyoming. *Geomorphology*, 57, pp. 217–233, 2004.

Author Index

WITPRESS ...for scientists by scientists

Advances in Fluid Mechanics VII

Edited by: M. RAHMAN, Dalhousie University, Canada and C.A. BREBBIA, Wessex Institute of Technology, UK

This book reflects the state of the art in fluid mechanics. The study of fluid mechanics involves various properties of the fluid, such as velocity, pressure, density and temperature, as functions of space and time. Featuring the latest developments, this book contains edited versions of the papers presented at the Seventh International Conference on Advances in Fluid Mechanics. Contributors from all round the world cover a wide range of topics, while particular emphasis is placed on new applications and research currently in progress.

   Invaluable to scientists, engineers and other professionals interested in the latest developments in theoretical and computational fluid mechanics, this volume encompasses: Convection, Heat and Mass Transfer; Experimental versus Simulation Methods; Computational Methods in Fluid Mechanics; Multiphase Flow; Boundary Layer Flow; Non-Newtonian Fluids; Hydraulics and Hydrodynamics; Wave Studies; Industrial Applications; Biofluids; Turbulence Flow; Permeability Problems; Environmental Fluid Mechanics; Petroleum Engineering Applications; Fluid Structure Interaction.

WIT Transactions on Engineering Sciences, Vol 59
ISBN: 978-1-84564-109-2   2008
apx 650pp
apx £214.00/US$428.00/€321.00

Fluid Structure Interaction and Moving Boundary Problems IV

Edited by: S.K CHAKRABARTI, Offshore Structure Analysis Inc., USA and C.A. BREBBIA, Wessex Institute of Technology, UK

Publishing papers presented at the Fourth International Conference on Fluid Structure Interaction, this book features contributions from experts specialising in this field on new ideas and the latest techniques. A valuable addition to this successful series and will be of great interest to mechanical and structural engineers, offshore engineers, earthquake engineers, naval engineers and any other experts involved in topics related to fluid structure interaction.

   Topics covered include: Hydrodynamic Forces; Response of Structures including Fluid Dynamics; Offshore Structure and Ship Dynamics; Fluid Pipeline Interactions; Structure Response to Serve Shock and Blast Loading; Vortex Shedding and Flow Induced Vibrations; Cavitation Effects in Turbo Machines and Pumps; Wind Effects on Bridges and Tall Structures; Mechanics of Cables, Risers; and Moorings; Biofluids and Biological Tissue Interaction; Computational Methods; Advances in Interaction problems in CFD; Experimental Studies and Validation; Vibrations and Noise; Free Surface Flows and Moving Boundary Problems.

WIT Transactions on the Built Environment, Vol 92
ISBN: 978-1-84564-072-9   2007   368pp
£125.00/US$245.00/€187.50

Atmosphere–Ocean Interactions

Volume 2

Edited by: W. PERRIE, Bedford Institute of Oceanography, Canada

The recent increase in levels of population and human development in coastal areas has led to a greater importance of understanding atmosphere–ocean interactions. Human activities that depend on the oceans require improvements in operational forecasts for marine weather and ocean conditions, and associated marine climate. This second volume on atmosphere–ocean interactions aims to present several of the key mechanisms that are important for the development of marine storms.

The book consists of eight chapters, each presenting separate topics that are predominantly self-contained. The first five chapters are concerned with marine observations and understanding their parameterizations as they relate to atmosphere–ocean systems. The subsequent three chapters consider some of the implications of these parameterizations, as related to applications in coupled atmosphere, ocean, and wave model systems.

Series: Advances in Fluid Mechanics, Vol 39
ISBN: 1-85312-929-1 2006 240pp
£79.00/US$142.00/€118.50

Solitary Waves in Fluids

Edited by: R.H.J. GRIMSHAW, Loughborough University, UK

After the initial observation by John Scott Russell of a solitary wave in a canal, his insightful laboratory experiments and the subsequent theoretical work of Boussinesq, Rayleigh and Korteweg and de Vries, interest in solitary waves in fluids lapsed until the mid 1960's with the seminal paper of Zabusky and Kruskal describing the discovery of the soliton. This was followed by the rapid development of the theory of solitons and integrable systems. At the same time came the realization that solitary waves occur naturally in many physical systems, and play a fundamental role in many circumstances.

The aim of this text is to describe the role that soliton theory plays in fluids in several contexts. After an historical introduction, the book is divided into five chapters covering the basic theory of the Korteweg-de Vries equation, and the subsequent application to free-surface solitary waves in water, internal solitary waves in coastal ocean and the atmospheric boundary layer, solitary waves in rotating flows, and to planetary solitary waves with applications to the ocean and atmosphere; The remaining chapter examines the theory and application of envelope solitary waves and the nonlinear Schrödinger equation to water waves.

Series: Advances in Fluid Mechanics, Vol 47
ISBN: 978-1-84564-157-3 2007 208pp
£70.00/US$130.00/€105.00

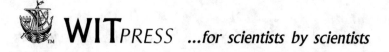

Instability of Flows

Edited by: **M. RAHMAN**, DalTech, Dalhousie University, Canada

A state-of-the art analysis of studies in the field of instability of flows, this book contains chapters by leading experts in fluid mechanics. The text brings together many important aspects of flow instabilities and one of the primary aims of the contributors is to determine fruitful directions for future advanced studies and research.

Contents: Preface; Contact-line Instabilities of Driven Liquid Films; Numerical Simulation of Three-dimensional Bubble Oscillations; Stratified Shear Flow – Instability and Wave Radiation; Instability of Flows; Stability, Transition and Turbulence in Rotating Cavities; A Comprehensive Investigation of Hydrodynamic Instability.

Series: Advances in Fluid Mechanics, Vol 41
ISBN: 1-85312-785-X   2005   248pp
£89.00/US$142.00/€133.50

Computational Methods in Multiphase Flow IV

Edited by: **A. MAMMOLI**, The University of New Mexico, USA and **C.A. BREBBIA**, Wessex Institute of Technology, UK

Fluid Dynamics is one of the most important topics of applied mathematics and physics. Together with complex flows and turbulence, multiphase flows remains one of the most challenging areas of computational mechanics, and even seemingly simple problems remain unsolved to date. Multiphase flows are found in all areas of technology, at all length scales and flow regimes. The fluids involved can be compressible or incompressible, linear or nonlinear. Because of the complexity of the problem, it is often essential to utilize advanced computational and experimental methods to solve the complex equations that describe them. Challenges in these simulations include nonlinear fluids, treating drop breakup and coalescence, characterizing phase structures, and many others.

This volume brings together work presented at the Fourth International Conference on Computational and Experimental Methods in Multiphase and Complex Flows. Featured topics include: Suspensions; Bubble and Drop Dynamics; Flow in Porous Media; Interfaces; Turbulent Flow; Injectors and Nozzles; Particle Image Velocimetry; Macroscale Constitutive Models; Large Eddy Simulation; Finite Volumes; Interface Tracking Methods; Biological Flows; Environmental Multiphase Flow; Phase Changes and Stochastic Modelling.

WIT Transactions on Engineering Sciences, Vol 56
ISBN: 978-1-84564-079-8   2007   416pp
£135.00/US$265.00/€202.50